the smallest wave

Dolores Reynals

Book Cover Design by Julia Rufener and book design by Alexa Ashley.

Printed and published in the United States of America.

Paperback ISBN: 978-607-29-5312-3
e-Book ISBN: 978-607-29-5313-0

Contents

For all the years I never lived near the sea, I am here now. I discovered that sometimes looking at it feels like being inside. The strength of a wave goes through you as it breaks. The magnitude of the mountains that surrounded me as a child was still and stable, another kind of peace. They protected me as I grew up. The eagles keeping watch. The sea does not stay still. Now I am learning what I missed. There is fierceness in the smallest wave, even the tiniest ones that reach the shore do what they do with all their might. They don't ask for permission and they don't care that they are small. Real fierceness comes from tenderness, I heard once. I can see that too in the sea. When I have looked at it, or swum in it for a long time, or when I have given it all my troubles and my thanks, I leave dizzy, as if I have made an exchange that went too far, like I have offered myself and got it in return.

The Rebellion

Baptism

When I was born, I was stabbed before I was out of my mother. The doctors had to burst a benign tumor to get me out and they used a scalpel for this on my lower back. They thought it was attached to my spine and calculated I would die instantly. Therefore, they did not bother with anesthetics. They sedated my mother after telling her I had died, and laid me on a table, waiting for the inevitable.

As I lay there waiting for death, a nurse saw me violently kicking and screaming and thought it best to try to baptize me, thinking there was still time to save me from original sin. Wrapping me in a blanket, she took me to the hospital chapel for an emergency baptism. The nurse performed the ceremony, sprinkling holy water on my forehead, and proclaiming my name *Alejandra Karina*, which she came up with herself. I've always liked that name because it sounds like Anna Karenina. The nurse then placed me back on that table, a newly baptized baby, to wait for my destiny. I used to imagine I was on a silver tray on that table. It seemed less cruel. As I lay there as Alejandra Karina, another nurse came by and saw me kicking and screaming as well, still alive. Not knowing about my first baptism, she went to check my mother's name, Cristina. She then took it upon herself to take me to the chapel for another emergency baptism, performing the ceremony again, holy water and all. She named me Maria Cristina.

Two hours and two baptisms later I had not stopped screaming. Evident now to the doctors that I had a chance of life, they decided to operate on me.

Afterwards, they let my father see me and said, triumphantly, "She may not be able to run a hundred meters, but she will live."

The doctors thought I would probably have trouble walking, but I walk really fast, just like my father. I never forget how lucky one is to do so. The scars on my body, which sometimes I have learned to love, remind me of my right to be here.

I got my third baptism the same month I was born. I can probably sin all I want. My parents wrapped it up, giving me all of my mother's names: Dolores María Cristina. Everyone just called her Cristina since she was a baby, and I was always Dolores, which is kind of like a bad joke. *Dolor* means "pain" in Spanish, but the plural *Dolores* means "pains." The name represents the Virgin Mary's suffering, her sorrows, "Our Lady of the Seven Dolors," as if that is all she ever did. The nickname for Dolores is often Lola, but that wasn't my luck. The two more exotic names from my first baptism didn't make it either. I got the Pain of Mary for Christ instead.

The first times I heard my birth story I thought I was probably not really allowed to be here. My parents used to tell me I was lucky to be alive. So I thought I was. I grew up believing my life was a miracle and that maybe I wasn't meant to live more than those two hours. That I cheated on God.

When I was little I would often sleep at my grandparents' home in a cot by their bed. During those times when I slept there, a wolf would visit me at night. It faced the doorway where the light came in, and turned its head to speak to me. It was not a big wolf, but I felt slightly scared the first time it showed up. I stood holding the bars of the crib that protected me, even though I knew it had not come to hurt me. It only visited me a few times and I now cannot remember what it said, but I listened to the words, lodged somewhere deep inside me.

I told my abuela about the wolf and she said that my uncle had recurring dreams in which frogs invaded the same cot. I wondered if I would see them too. But I knew they only came for my uncle just as the wolf only visited me.

I would lie awake at night a few years later when I was seven, knowing that the wolf held the mystery of existence. I prayed that it would return to share it with me, and that somehow I would understand. I never thought of asking anyone else. But the wolf never did return, and I had to look for the answers alone.

The Women on the Wall

"Abuelita Lola lived to be a hundred and five," said my abuela, pointing at her own grandmother's patient old face in a sepia-toned photograph hanging in the corridor of her apartment. I was still little and she had picked me up so I could see. There were five faces in the picture, the edges of their bodies disappearing in a ghostly blur. The first face she pointed at was my great-great-grandmother, the first Dolores in the family as far as we knew. Abuelita Lola from Granada with the cool, sexy name was wearing all black like a García Lorca character. Her eyes were almost closed as she was by this time blind. I decided then I would live until one hundred and five like her too, if not more.

Maybe it was the pull of the spell. I am the fourth one with her name in our family. But not Lola, just Dolores.

Even sexier than Lola is Lolita, but that was taken by my abuela. She was also in the picture in the bottom row, smiling as usual, next to her two sisters when they were still young. I just got to be Dolo, or "Doloreeee!" without the "s" when the Andalusian women called my name.

Next to Abuelita Lola was my great-grandmother Laura, looking glamorous and smiling, with big hoop earrings and finely plucked eyebrows like an old movie star. She had died not long ago, when I was five, but until then she had been my bisabuela, whom I loved to visit in her apartment around the corner from us. Always loud and cheerful, shouting Andalusian and swearing when she mixed-up her great-grand-children's names. "¡Puñeta! ¡¿Cómo te llamas?!"

My mother said she knew lots of dirty jokes.

I wondered, what kind of woman would I be, positioned on that wall? Whom would I look like? Would I live a long patient life? Would I be beautiful like Laura?

When I plucked out almost all my eyebrows in the nineties, and I had a thick unibrow like nobody in the family, I used this photo as a guide. My abuela almost cried. "The beautiful thing about you!" She sounded just like Amy March in Little Women saying, "Jo! Your one beauty!" when Jo cuts all her hair off. Lolita said my eyebrows might not grow back. I thought I finally looked cool. Maybe that's who I would be on the wall: the one with the nineties eyebrows, like the girls on MTV.

Holding Hands with a Stranger

His name was Mateo and he looked like the Little Prince with his blond curls. Our mums had imposed our relationship on us as a cute joke or something when we were three and four. We just used to play gauchos on horses in the hall of the nursery as we waited for them to pick us up. We obediently assumed our roles. Soon I looked at my big Pepona doll made of cloth sitting on a chair in my bedroom and saw her small hoop earrings as wedding rings. I ripped them out, because that was the next thing to do. I tried one on and my finger's blood circulation stopped. An adult had to use a lot of soap to get it off while telling me how dangerous this had been and I wondered if this time we were going to have to cross the street to the hospital. Cancel the wedding.

Mateo was a year ahead of me in our nursery school. My mother was the headmistress and the nursery was in her childhood home, a colonial-style white house with a galleria around a black- and-white tiled patio. The front was painted light green with a drawing of a frog on the wall and the words "El Sapito," The Little Frog, written above.

As you walked into the house, the first room to the right was small, and my favorite, where we saw cartoon films shown via a projector. My mother's office was in her old bedroom, and she would have faced the entrance if she ever sat down for a second at her desk. She always flashed by me, running around between the nursery, our home next door where my baby triplet brother and sisters Maria Julia, Maria José, and Martín were with the nanny, and around town. Looking immaculate as if none of this existed, with her tailored outfits and her perfect bob, the side fringe she occasionally brushed away from her eyes was the only thing that ever came out of place. When I looked at her I thought I had the best mum in the world. I knew the other kids agreed. I had to share her with everyone, here and at home where we both got lost among so many other kids and grown-ups. I wanted her attention, to have her to myself, like when I was too young to remember. This was probably why I started misbehaving. When a teacher caught me chewing gum I was taken aside and told that I had to be the example for the other children in the nursery. The same at home with the triplets. I always found more gum. The stuff was in fashion and going around. By misbehaving I was getting an identity outside of being the elder sister. My imposed relationship with Mateo gave me something similar.

16

There was a ceramic ornament in our apartment on a small side table by the front door. It was a white, rectangular box. I had picked it up and was analyzing it when my father took it from my hands to set it back in its place. "Your boyfriend's mum and dad gave this to us as a wedding present," he said.

He loved teasing me about my "boyfriend" and any boy he ever found out about later.

"He's not my boyfriend!"

I was angry as I realized this was all their idea, and because Mateo had suddenly, out of the blue, not been nice to me. He had recently sort of dumped me. Or had I dumped him?

Mateo lived in the building next door on Zapata Street. Both buildings were the construction of my great-grandfather Pepe who had arrived in Mendoza from the south of Spain in 1910. As soon as he turned sixteen his parents sent him on a boat to join his older brother Manuel, escaping the economic crisis and military service. He began working with him in a food store, which led them to one day having their own supermarket and finally starting a building company. Papá Pepe's name was affixed to the building's entrance on a brass sign nailed to the marble wall. I could not read it then, but knew it said José López Vilchez. He had died long ago but his wife, my great-grandmother Laura, who had arrived with her parents and lived in another building around the corner, was still around. She had never fully moved to Argentina. She went to the other side of the world to end up marrying someone from the hills an hour's drive away from the beach where she was born, in Calahonda. Mendoza winters were too cold for her, and every year she and Pepe would leave their children in boarding school while they took a boat to enjoy the summer in their homeland.

My mother owned our apartment in the building, and all my second cousins lived around us. We were on the first floor, so we had a patio. In it there was a laundry area where I had seen the backs of many women, some I knew and some hired for the task, who washed the triplets' cloth diapers day in and day out, by hand. On the opposite wall, the side where I would exit into the patio from our apartment, I had a little plastic house which was nothing fancy, just like our real home, with furniture drawn on the walls that resembled a living room, a table and chairs, and a kitchen. I would step out from our real kitchen into the middle of the red patio and call out, "Mateo!"

Mateo's blond curls would show up, hit by the light at his window, which overlooked my patio. We would shout out some conversation à la Romeo and Juliet.

The same way I did, Mateo would call out my name and someone would let me know and I would run out to the patio to greet him.

One day we were going on vacation to Chile and I went to say goodbye, with my red sunglasses on. I shouted out Mateo's name but he didn't come so I shouted twice more.

"Mateooooooooo!"

"What do you waaaant?!" He said, coming outside.

What? That was not what he was supposed to say. "I wanted to tell you that I am going to
the beach, to sunbathe, and you're staying here!"

With that I ran into my plastic house. I don't think I remember any childhood dialogue as vividly as this anti-Romeo-and-Juliet scene in my unbearably sunny patio.

There was another boy who must have been short like me because we both stood next to each other at the front of the line at school, and I would hold his hand. His straight brown hair was cut like a Playmobil doll. To me he was really dreamy. I used to put my head on his shoulder when we formed the line. I must have seen that somewhere. Or was it instinct?

A year or so later I was standing in my abuela's kitchen, right by the trash can, crying my eyes out. Something must have made me remember that boy I held hands with and realize that I had once been "in love," or so I felt that day. I thought it must be wrong, because there was something unbearable about it. And now I was standing there, my abuela asking me, dear god, what was I crying so much about, and all I could say was, "It's just that I was in...I was in...in..." I think I never said it. It was around the time my father called me Mary Magdalene and Sarah Bernhardt alternatively.

Buried Treasures

There's two types of alone. The one you don't expect and the one you crave. As a child, my maternal grandparents' apartment was the place to be loved and spoiled and left to play without interruptions, except for fresh scones coming out of the oven or my grandfather's opera sounding loud on the record player. I walked around the apartment in my pajamas pretending I was an opera singer, adults half laughing saying, "How beautiful you sing," which let me know it was not beautiful at all. My parents had their hands full running their own businesses full-time and with us kids as we became savages as soon as we all could walk. Always fighting about something. Fighting for space. Nannies would cry and lose it. One of us was often sent to our grandparents' house to make it easier for whoever was looking after us. There we got all the attention we could not have at home.

My brother Martín would sit on the floor in front of my abuelo's armchair where he would be reading and ask him a million questions, which he gladly answered with stories my brother loved to hear, while Lolita yelled, "Bruno! Please leave the child to play. Stop talking to him!"

I loved being the only child there when it was my turn. I had silence and privacy, both impossible at home. I would make my own cinema by putting a flashlight on top of a shoebox on my aunt Adriana's bed in order to hold it, facing the closet doors. Then I would pull the heavy blinds down, turn off the lights, and move one or two small dolls in front of the flashlight, projecting their shadows. And I could at least watch a real film until the end without being interrupted. Two of my favorites on TV were *Mary Poppins* and *The Sound of Music*. Mary Poppins had started to invade my imagination. My superstitious Andalusian abuela would hurry towards me when she saw me jumping from my aunt's bed to the floor holding an umbrella, pretending to be Mary Poppins about to fly.

"Nooooo mijita! It's bad luck to open an umbrella indoors!" She would grab and close the umbrella. I would then shut the door and open the umbrella again.

The scene in *Mary Poppins* where laughing makes them float up to the ceiling while having tea at uncle Albert's is still my favorite. I would lie on the floor looking up, imagining I too was stuck to the ceiling, looking down. Furniture had flown up with me. In *Poltergeist*, another film my grandmother let me watch, my favorite scene was when the woman is invaded by the spirit in her bedroom and is dragged up to the ceiling as well.

The following year, I was watching *The Sound of Music* when Lolita came into the TV room.

"You know, that is the same lady who plays Mary Poppins. Her name is Julie Andrews. She is an actress."

Whaaaat?! But they were different women. I mentioned the hair. One woman was blonde and one brunette.

"That could be a wig," Lolita said.

I got closer to the screen and looked carefully at her face. Lolita was right. It was the same woman. It was the most exciting thing I'd ever found out, even if it killed the magic of Mary Poppins. If the actress could do that, go into another world, then so could I. I could escape my reality, my home, and go beyond what was in front of me.

There was a woman at my grandparents' house whose name was Argentina, like our country. She had worked at their home since they married and helped with the housework and five children. Her voice is still faint in my mind because I was born when she was already old. She had a daughter called Carmen who lived with them in the house too. Carmen called her Mami, which is short for Mamá, mother. So everyone called her the same.

Mami's smile was slow, wide, and deep, and her eyes sparkled every day. She had white hair contrasting with her dark skin, short, and combed back. She always wore a skirt that stretched open at the knees when she sat down, and a short-sleeved button-up blouse. Now she didn't work anymore and sat crocheting with Lolita at the kitchen table while watching the news or the telenovela de la tarde. The wool threads, as did the needles, came out of a plastic supermarket bag that lay at her feet. She would take out a wool ball from the bag to gather the thread she had been using before changing to another color.

Mami had many treasures in her supermarket bag, and she inspired me to have my own. She let me sit with her on the balcony looking at the square, on the side without the geraniums, where I kept my turtle which didn't live very long, and where the green plant with no flowers was, the one that I loved touching. It had brown elevated dots on each one of its thin, undulated leaves.

"Mami, what's wrong with this plant?" I asked. "Why do these leaves have dots?"

"Because God put them there. There is nothing wrong with it."

She gave me thread and beads and showed me how to make bracelets. It was the first time I had something that wasn't for sharing. Nobody opened my supermarket bag. I put my things in it, whatever my things were. Out of Mami's bag came threads of wool of all colors. She had treasures I never knew of because I never looked inside. I silently under-stood. I sat by her and we both made something. I thought my bracelets were elegant. They had grown-up beads.

Sometimes I was a bit afraid of Mami because she was quieter than my abuela, and much older, and there was a lot I didn't know about her like who was her mum. I never felt like I should ask. She was a mystery and I followed her around everywhere. Maybe it was her calm soul, her quiet wisdom that captivated me. She knit me a crochet blanket for my birthday. The squares are lined in pink. My mother brings it out for me when I visit in winter.

Impure Thoughts
Commandment Number 9

My grandparents lived in an apartment with a balcony that faced Independencia Square, the main square downtown with a fountain in front of a big outdoor stage, and a museum beneath. An artisans fair took place there during the weekend.

I would sleep in my aunt Adriana's bedroom because she had twin beds. When I became old enough we played cards before bedtime, always betting for something. She still owes me a few sweaters, knit by her, and money that has now devalued into nothing.

"Desgraciada!" she would call me every time I won.

At night I begged Adriana to stop reading and turn off the lamp on the bedside table between the twin beds. She would then place a big portrait of Lolita and her sister Coca as kids in ridiculous dresses, which they hated, between the lamp and my side, and carry on reading through the thickest glasses you can imagine, almost placing the book on them. I would turn around and face the wallpaper with big pink roses and get sleepy finding shapes among the petals.

Adriana never married, I remember my grandmother telling people when talking about her daughter. She was overly protected as a young girl because her myopia was minus thirty-something. Even with glasses she did not see completely but was brave enough to go out into the street and walk all around downtown alone, all the time.

When she was fourteen and the family was spending time at my great-grandmother's house away from the city, Adriana met a boy, a friend of the gardener's. He asked her to be his girlfriend. One day she brought him into the house, and my grandmother said she was never to meet with him again. That she had to be careful because of her bad sight, as she clearly could not distinguish whom she should hang out with or not. The boy was clearly from the other side of the canal and train tracks, of a very humble background. One could tell by his clothes, which Adriana could not have noticed, and if she had, she probably would not have cared.

I am not sure if it was the reason my aunt never brought any boy home ever again but it could have been. She studied philosophy in university and devoted herself to reading, knitting, and mostly, the church.

She once helped me with religious studies homework, when I was in primary school before my first communion. I was ill in bed and we were going through the Ten Commandments. I asked what number nine meant, because at school they had not really explained it.

"Thou shalt not have impure thoughts or desires."

What did impure thoughts mean?

"If you ever imagine, for example, I don't know, that a boy would hug you," she said. That was a mortal sin.

I was speechless at that. Maybe she was trying to protect me. Just like I was trying to protect her, always stealing the packet of twenty cigarettes from her bag or drawer and emptying it into the toilet.

The Price you Pay

When I was eleven I got to fly from Mendoza to Buenos Aires with my father to go to my cousin Claudia's wedding. My sweet big cousin whom I never got to see. I would stay at my aunt Silvia's house with her daughter Bárbara who was one year older than me. She grew up in the big city while I grew up in the province of Mendoza. Since early childhood we both wanted to get along but always ended up fighting instead. We had changed since then, and we did have things in common, like we both enjoyed reading. But different kinds of books. She read things like Jane Austen's novels and me, the *Babysitter's Club*. We also liked playing pranks on people, like that time we spent a summer in Chile together and nobody knew us in the building, and we locked people in the elevator for a bit because we figured out where the control panel was, that kind of thing.

Bárbara seemed like a grown-up. She was an outstanding student. She could hold an intelligent conversation with adults and impress them with a few nonchalant words. I was the mischievous, most likely to get kicked-out of school (eventually kicked-out of school) one. I had braces and glasses, red Bermudas, a striped t-shirt, and my white Nikes when I arrived at her house with my father. Hers had recently passed away from a stroke. He had been the cook in the house so we were standing by the kitchen counter while my auntie tried to heat-up something that was ready made.

Bárbara reached over and touched my hair. "I am so jealous of your long, wavy hair," she said.

I had never really thought about my hair until that day. She took me to her room to show me what she was going to wear for the wedding: A shimmery navy-blue dress with spaghetti straps. Sexy but classy.

"What will you wear?"

I had not given any thought to this either. As soon as I did, I was embarrassed. My mother had decided—she always decided with real OCD—on my sailor dress that I had been wearing for years. I always loved it, but now I saw that it really was a kid's dress. It was white with pleats on the short skirt, a sailor-blue V stripe on the chest, with flowers embroidered in the middle of the V. Bárbara brought out baby blue eyeshadow and opened it for me to see. I had seen women wearing this shade in magazines and on TV, so striking and fashionable, so unlike me.

"Don't tell my mum I bought this," she said. She was going to apply it after the church ceremony, when my aunt would lose sight of us. "There will be boys at the wedding," she said. That next day in the downtown mansion that was rented out for the big event, Bárbara and I locked ourselves in one of the bathrooms where she started applying the baby blue eyeshadow. I looked at her reflection in the mirror.

"We have to make a plan to catch the wedding bouquet," she said.

"Ay no. I don't want it."

"You don't want to catch the bouquet?! Okay, we have to make a plan so I catch it."

"Okay. If I catch it, I will pass it to you."

"Great! Would you like some eyeshadow?"

I looked in the mirror and was sure that it would not improve my sailor look one bit. I hated my mother for making me wear a child's outfit and hated myself for not having any idea how ridiculous I would look and feel in the now too-short in a non-attractive way dress. I declined the eyeshadow.

When the bouquet-throwing time came, Bárbara and I made our way towards the dance floor, which began to get crowded with women. I followed Bárbara right into the middle of the crowd.

"Throw it to meeeee! Throw it to meeeee!" shouted the women.

Claudia got on top of a table at the front, teasing to throw the bouquet in one direction or another, towards which the women moved, pushing and elbowing each other. Screaming. I slowly began moving out of everyone's way. Bárbara hadn't noticed I wasn't right next to her anymore. Great, because I was not so sure about this. I didn't know exactly what was so disturbing to me about it all, but I wanted to be as far away from it as possible. I had soon made my way out of the crowd. What was wrong with me? Maybe I am not a real woman? Was every woman in the room who wasn't married there?

Yes, they were.

Are there any women out there in the world who don't want to fight and scream for this silly bouquet? I hope they do exist.

Standing there I realized I was not a child anymore but I was not ready to grow up either. Being a woman looked stupid. I could see my cousin Bárbara looking for me, so I ran to the other end of the room, where my father was having a conversation with another man. I pretended to be interested, turning my back to the crazy bouquet scene. Perfect.

My father was in his grey suit, always elegant in the same uniform, always talking, never silent, now talking to this man. Then from out of nowhere I felt something land right on my head. Before I reflexively grabbed it, I knew what it was. I brought it down and looked at it in disbelief and then looked at my father, half laughing.

"Mijita, you got the bouquet!" he said.

"Shsssss!" I pleaded, holding the flowers down, knowing they belonged to Bárbara. She was next to me in a flash. I looked at her for help, to take it away from me somehow.

She motioned, "Hurry up pass it," but the photographer was already there, followed by my cousin Claudia. Mierda. I posed. I wish I had this photograph today to see my face. I said to Bárbara, "Here, take it," although I had started to feel it as mine. A promise is a promise. But she said it was too late.

"I cannot believe you got the bouquet."

Me neither.

Right after, all the women were pulling the long laces coming out from the wedding cake. Strings that hold little symbols at one end of them, hidden inside the cake, like a heart, a lock, a ring. If you get this ring it also means you will get married next. Knowing that I probably should stay away from the cake now to give the other women a chance, I still decided to join them. I was not afraid of them anymore. Maybe I was now a proper woman. Maybe I just wanted to tease them a little bit. God was merciful and I only got a padlock.

After the wedding ended, I took the bouquet with me and put it in a plastic bag to take it on the plane back. It was a beautiful, small bouquet of white roses and a few small dried flowers as decoration. I tried to find the meaning of catching the bouquet. Maybe some things happen whether you want them to or not. Or maybe one day I would genuinely be like, "Holy shit, I am married. How did this happen?"

I also kind of liked that the flowers had landed on my head. I was pleased that those crazy ladies desperate to be married didn't get them, even if insensitively so. I knew there was a message for me here. I packed the bouquet and took it home. Then I put it on top of my chest of drawers in my room, and once the roses had dried I put it back in the plastic bag and kept it on a high shelf in my closet until I knew what to do with it, because in a way I felt it did not belong to me (or that I didn't deserve it). I found the bouquet every now and then and peeked at the dry flowers, proud that I had them, every time wondering if it was true that I would get married because of this.

My cousin Claudia got divorced a couple of years later. I was shocked. How could a wedding make love last so little? This reality hurt me. Was this not the ultimate couple commitment and a promise of love, or a blessing from your god to your love? This was as mad to me as the ladies pushing each other on the dance floor for the promise of a promise. I went into my closet and looked at the bouquet again. Maybe it meant I deserved all the things that all the other women wanted, wherever I decided to stand.

Rebel with a Cause

I was seventeen and a new student at my neighborhood Catholic school. It was my last year of high school and I had been invited to leave from my previous super-demanding school with long hours and compulsory English every day because of bad behavior, which I thought was an exaggeration. I had begged my parents to let me go to a normal school. I had promised to be the best student and have the best behavior if they let me. I convinced them, and myself, but my rebellious side could not be tamed so easily, not even now that I was older.

One day I put the famous statement *The people united will never be defeated* to the test, which I then thought was Che Guevara's, although all I discovered was the power of one. Our headmistress Hermana Amable, Sister Kindness, announced that students were expected to take a big exam at the end of the year. We would be tested on every single subject. The program had been changed and no one told us in advance. If we failed the end-of-year physics exam, for example, all the exams we sat for during the year, for each unit of the subject, which we had already taken, would not count and we would have to retake the entire subject again in the summer. I thought she was being very unfair. Most of all I was terrified that I was going to fail all of these exams, as I was not a good student and every exam I had passed was passed by the skin of my teeth. I went around the school asking students what they thought of this and everyone I spoke to agreed. It was not fair.

I began organizing a very well-justified protest in the school patio and went by each classroom collecting signatures. Both my sisters, including Maria Julia, a star student my teachers liked to compare me to, signed without a question, and her friends followed. I was impressed by the turnout.

The day of the protest came and we all gathered on the patio. We must have been a couple of hundred students. Teenagers from the first year of high school to the last. I thought, the nuns cannot kick two hundred students out of school. We have power. We sat cross-legged on the red-tiled floor, clapped our hands twice and then clapped them twice against our knees while we chanted:

"Nooooo nos vamos nada, queeeee nos saquen a patadas, nooooo nos vamos nada, queeee nos saquen a patadas."

Which means:

"We are not leaving, you will have to kick us out."

Hermana Amable came out and stood in front of us. She shouted that if we didn't get up straight away and stop this nonsense, she would have us all sign the discipline book. It was kept in Hermana Amable's office, and misbehaving students would have to write their name within it. For each incident. Sometimes you had to write two or three signatures, depending on the gravity of your crime. In the past I got many signatures for disappearing from class, throwing a shoe across the classroom, and for constantly interrupting class because I could not stay still or quiet. Also for listening to my Walkman instead of the teacher, hiding it in my hair. And, when I was younger, for releasing a little mouse into the classroom. But this time was different.

"You know that after twenty signatures you will be kicked out of school," Hermana Amable threatened. I had about ten, but I knew I would be fine.

"Well, you all will get ten signatures from this. I am giving you a chance to get up now."

We all knew they could not kick everyone out. Nobody got up. Success. We chanted.

"Let me tell you I have no problem kicking you all out of school. No problem at all, and I will do it," Hermana Amable insisted, now furious.

All the girls who could not stand the idea of a signature in the discipline book stood up. About half of them. I would be kicked out for sure, but I knew they would not expel about a hundred students. We carried on chanting. Hermana Amable threatened to immediately call all of our parents. I looked at my friends and they seemed to be standing strong. But lots of other students stood up. Did they not think this through before putting their signature down?

A few of my friends stood up saying things like, "My mum will kill me."

"But she won't if we all stay." I replied.

They left. When my good friend Natalia got up, that made me think everyone was a liar. She saw that this made me upset.

"Sorry, my friend. There are just a few of us now. We will be expelled. You should get up."

I said fine, as you wish. Really, it was my plan and why should anyone go along. But everyone felt strongly about it. That was what they had said.

Soon I was alone on the patio. I clapped my hands to the song without stopping, staring ahead. I just changed the lines from plural to singular.

Hermana Amable and the "preceptora," the one in charge of behavior, stood by me. The preceptora was a slim, blonde woman with a garçon haircut and a friendly face, a sense of humor, and a lot of mercy. They explained that if I didn't get up I would be kicked out of school.

But if I got up, it would mean that I had deserted my own fight. I carried on. After a bit of debating between them, they each took me by an armpit and dragged me along the patio and up to the office. I carried on singing as I was pulled up the stairs. I was a bit scared of being kicked out of school and having to go to night school with the older people, but I was going to walk my talk.

After Hermana Amable left, the preceptora said she would not make me sign the book ten times. Just enough so I had one signature left before being expelled. She asked me please not to do that to myself. I did not like that she took

37

pity on me, but I was relieved.

Almost getting kicked out of school was not as tragic to me as my disappointment that day in people, in myself for being so naïve, and in the failed protest. My friends had let me down. I thought we were in the protest together. They sounded as enthusiastic as I was. Were they lying? Do people ever think things through when they join anything? What makes someone say they are committed to something, to then not be? Maybe to them it was just a game. Maybe I was rigid.

Maybe with more important matters, like Che Guevara's cause, things go differently. I asked my friends and they mainly answered, "It was your idea, not ours."

The exams did not happen. The school changed the rules again, surely not because of my protest, but maybe it did help. Maybe the world reacts in mysterious ways.

The Calling

The Loneliness of Freedom

The need to escape runs in my family. I was ready now for my first escape. I had been longing for it, envisioning it when I looked out the window at the mountains during class. I wanted to go exploring by myself anywhere else, to see another scene, another landscape. To experience how other people lived in the world. A calling that was my very own, strong enough that I could not question it. And now an opportunity had finally arrived.

When I was finishing my last year of high school, my Spanish uncle Enrique from Granada had been in Mendoza for a visit, and this time he invited me to go back with him. I was dying to go but I had three subjects to retake in the summer, so I could not travel yet. Even if I could wait until the end of the summer when I was to pass those exams, and travel then on my own, my parents were completely against me going, or getting away with anything anymore. I had promised them that I would be the best student ever at the new school because it was less demanding, but I had not delivered. Quite the opposite had happened, in fact. I had relaxed there and ended up with worse grades than ever.

I swore I would pass my summer exams but that was not enough. I cried and begged, lying on their bed like it was the end of the world, and it was for me at that time. I deeply regretted any school failing if it meant I didn't get to go on this trip. I longed to go to Andalusía. It was far away and exciting like my great-grandmother Laura's accent. She had sent my mother to meet the family and immerse in the culture once she had finished high school. She took her to proper flamenco dance lessons, in caves with gypsies. It was technically a family tradition. Why would it not be my turn now? My mother had lived in her aunt's home in the city of Granada. Then with another aunt who owned a hotel in the seaside town of Calahonda, my great-grandmother's hometown, where she and her cousins stayed and sometimes helped look after guests, although I knew this was not their main activity; poolside lounging and partying was more like it. Standing by the bed looking at my pleading act, my parents tried to stay firm and say no, but I knew they were struggling.

My parents had both lived abroad; my mother for long periods of time, years in Chile and Spain. When she wasn't abroad she would date foreign men like Michelle from Switzerland, a ski-season boyfriend who brought her the first bottle of sunblock she ever had. Or Jean-Luc from Paris, also a ski boyfriend who many years later became her friend and a friend of my father's too. The southern hemisphere has all the European skiers during our winters from June to August. I saw how different they were, always carrying more mountain gear than we do, tanning redder around their ski goggles. I loved when anything different to my everyday life was revealed to me. Also, foreigners saw our land with new eyes, which made us see and appreciate our own place again. They commented on the height of our mountains and how steep and more challenging the ski slopes were here. I skied on those difficult slopes, first with an instructor, then slowly alone or with my mother who had no fear when skiing was involved. I loved listening to the foreigners' accents. I already knew that languages are hard. They take work if you want to speak beyond, "How much is it?" and "Where is the bathroom?" I knew this because I was bad at them until I put in the real work when I had no way out, which became agonizing when verbs were involved in our English and French classes at school.

My father learnt French and English from his grandma who taught these languages at university, and some Portuguese from a Brazilian girlfriend when he was young. My mother had learnt French at school and almost became a teacher, but she left her studies for other ventures, eventually opening a travel agency. I grew up hearing stories of other places and looking at brochures, longing to inhabit those images of beaches out of my desert in the mountains of Mendoza. A big city in what used to be a desert, but still. I wanted to see different streets, different cities.

I wanted to see the place where so many family stories came from. I used to look through my mother's albums, although a lot of those photos were of weeks on a boat, and her sailor boyfriend, and then her bullfighter boyfriend once she had arrived in Spain. There was a small silver statue of a man on a horse, sitting by a portrait of my father and uncle, at home. The bullfighter gave her that. He was a rejoneador, the ones who fight the bull on a horse. I like them even less than the ones who fight standing.

To my surprise I passed the exams in summer school with As and discovered I actually liked French. I almost preferred studying in the summer, everything at once in a month instead of taking a year for it. My mother had mercy and wanted to follow this new family tradition. The longing for Spain she had inherited from her mother and grandmother was strong and she didn't want to lose that connection. For better or worse, I was her link at this moment.

Now that I was going, really going, I planned a goodbye party with my friends, picked the clothes I would take, and gathered half my CDs: Pearl Jam, Oasis, No Doubt, Café Tacuba, Lenny Kravitz, Jamiroquai, Los Rodriguez, Los Abuelos de la Nada, Alanis Morissette, Soul Asylum, Soda Stereo, the Offspring, and a few Bon Jovi because they were the second band I ever liked after Roxette. I had a very big suitcase.

My uncle Enrique picked me up from the airport in Granada. His wife, Charo, waited for us at home. She was as I had seen in photographs. Tall, very elegant, with short blonde hair and sharp blue eyes. Warm but strict. They had five children. Ana, who still lived at home, was the youngest at twenty-one. I imagined that having a far-away relative from Argentina who was going to stay until who knows when could be very intrusive, but Ana was only friendly with me. I was given my cousin Enriquito's bedroom as he had just gotten married. The bed that pulled out from the wall was left out. I had a shelf beside it where I put all my CDs. Next to the bed was a window overlooking Camino de Ronda, right on the edge of downtown Granada.

I wondered what my aunt actually thought of me arriving without a plan. I also wondered what she thought of anyone from Argentina, a faraway country her husband would often leave for, on long business trips on his own.

I unpacked and I went to sleep, excited for my new life in Spain.

There was not much work advertised in the morning newspaper, even less than in Mendoza. I had saved enough money from a translating job during the last year of high school, but I knew it wouldn't last very long. I needed a job if I was not going to university that year. I was not sent on a vacation, just a change of location. Maybe I could study something here too. I walked up the hill to Casa de Porras, an arts center that to my surprise looked abandoned until further notice. I saw the theatre and photography programs advertised and posted on their windows outside, but they were starting in the autumn. It was spring.

During the mornings I helped my aunt Charo when she made lunch, even though she had it all under control, for her adult children who visited at this time of day, although usually not all five of them at once: Yayo, Cristina, Enriquito, Macarena, and Ana who already lived there. Preparing rice with squid in its ink, cutting the strawberries for dessert, re-using frying oil.

"Mothers never get burnt!" Charo used to say as she quickly handled the hottest trays and plates. I helped set the table at 2 pm as the television by the table played *3rd Rock from the Sun*, dubbed in Spanish.

"Oye, Deeck!" I loved how they pronounced his name. Everything was dubbed and this was very unusual to me. Even at the cinema most movies were dubbed so that it was rare to see the original version of any foreign language film. My cousin Ana and her friends said they had never heard Brad Pitt's real voice, and they didn't even want to.

After lunch everyone fell asleep on the sofas that were actually our seats at the table. They put their feet up on a heater under it in the middle, whether it was on or off, and all dozed off for about half an hour, with the TV on, before going back to work. I never could fall asleep, and just watched the show with gossip about celebrities of which I knew nothing.

My aunt Charo had two boutiques in town, run by her and my cousins Cristina, Macarena, and Ana, where they sold haberdashery as well as traditional Gitana accessories for the local parties of La Cruz. The Día de La Cruz celebration on the third of May dates back to the seventeenth century, when there was an alabaster cross built in the neighborhood of Santa Cruz and all the neighbors gathered to dance. Nowadays the women wear the traditional flamenco dresses on this day, so my aunt sold lots of accessories from her shop for the street parties. Big red necklaces, hoops and colorful earrings, hair accessories like big flowers. I went on a day trip to Seville with them to buy from the wholesalers. The streets of Seville had a bit more glamour than Granada. Seville was bigger, with more going on. It was the capital of flamenco and my first glimpses of the city just made me want to walk more and more. But I had to stay with the family and quickly return to the car when the buying was finished, to drive the pretty and windy road on the hills back to Granada, hoping that one day I would see the excitement of Seville.

We returned a few weeks later with my cousin Ana and her friends for the main Easter parties and parades in early April. Seville Easter processions were wild. All the big saint figures from the churches are taken out for the parade in the evening, held up underneath sometimes by dozens of people as some platforms and saints are huge.

The people carrying the saints are called Costaleros. Now and then from beneath a platform a leg pokes out for a stretch, or a head comes up for air. Between carriages are groups of people in traditional penitent robes, capes and pointy hats, which to this day scare me. Candles everywhere, trumpets and singing.

A lot of onlookers from the sides of the street were drunk on local wine by 4 pm, especially on Manzanilla wine, my personal killer, and kept going. I still didn't see much of Seville this time. I was much younger than Ana and could not keep up with the drinking. My mother had warned me about how much they drink in Spain, and had tried to give me a bit of wine at lunch and dinner every day to "train" me. It didn't work.

Back in Granada the parties went on. On the day of La Cruz in May, Ana and I went to get our Gitana polka-dot dresses from the wardrobe. I had not taken flamenco lessons like my mother did—a doctor had warned me because of an impending scoliosis that I shouldn't—but at least I could wear the dress and look the part. I could put on a loud necklace and a flower in my hair, take a fan with me, maybe even place a mantilla on my head like in that picture of my mother's when she was two-years old. Ana opened a wardrobe in my room and showed me the dresses. I would wear a white one with green polka dots. But my aunt's voice stopped us from the hallway outside my room. It was raining and there was no way she would let us ruin the dresses.

"What if we promise to really look after them? Por favor, Charo. This may be the only chance I get to dress as a Gitana," I said.

I had been waiting for this, but she would not have us trailing a white dress on the street or the dirty bar floors, and our vehicles were scooters so we had no chance. I said to Ana that we should wait until she went to take her siesta and do it anyway. She came into the room to say that she had heard me. There was no fooling aunt Charo.

We went out at lunchtime in stupid civilian clothes. All the Gitanas filled the streets and the bars. Manzanilla wine had gone to my head by 4 pm and someone had to give me a ride back home on their scooter before I collapsed. I woke up hours later with Ana shaking me, asking if I had slept enough, because it was now 10 pm and the party was in full swing. Around 4 am someone else had to drop me back on their scooter again.

Those days I also spent time with my cousin Macarena, my uncle's middle daughter, the hippie one with messy curly hair she had chopped off, because she never had known what to do with it, she said. She always brought ice cream with her and we talked about the days when she had lived in London. I wanted to know all about it. I really felt that maybe one day I would spend time there. In Granada she lived up the hill where the gypsies were, in the Albaicín neighborhood with a square that was a huge viewpoint from which to see the great Alhambra, the famous Islamic palace. This neighborhood was another world. There were caves there. The ones where my mother had learnt to dance, with a tape player on the floor and the rhythmic clapping of her teachers. Some caves were bars, some homes, some for parties and dancing.

Macarena took me around on her big motorcycle, showing me the parts of Granada I would have otherwise not seen. Soon enough I had been all around the city until I knew it by heart. I could get everywhere by foot from the apartment into the windy streets, past churches and ruins and into the Alhambra, where I went again and again to get lost in its gardens and palaces. Then Ana and her friends brought me along to all the bars and clubs downtown and I got to see the lively nightlife of Granada. Even in clubs, between the electronic music and nineties hits, at some point they would play flamenco and everyone there knew how to move their arms and hands, or just one of them if you were holding a drink, for those five minutes.

I loved the city and it felt familiar already, although I didn't see myself living there for much longer because I wasn't finding it easy to get work. I had to find an alternative if this was not happening, but I didn't know what to do. Going back to Argentina so soon was out of the question for me. I wanted to travel around Spain and Europe.

One day when we were eating ice cream at my uncle's table, Macarena said she could tell I was lost. She was right. I couldn't dance flamenco, so why was I even here? I felt useless, without a purpose, and homesick, to my disbelief.

Why did my mother ever come here for so long? What was she doing, just dancing?

"What would you like to do? Now and when you go back home?" Macarena asked.

I said that before going back to study theatre and translation to not starve to death as my parents had told me I would, I wanted to travel, and also to work so I could pay for it.

Macarena told my cousin Enriquito about my situation. He was always going to the mountains to look after the family's land and his "children," the horses, and he asked his friends in the touristy mountain areas if there were any jobs available, right before the summer. Luckily one of his friends found me a position as an apprentice tour and mountain guide. I would train until I was ready to be a guide by the time the tourists came. I was thrilled.

The location was in the Alpujarras, a group of old white towns connected by trails and little roads, up in the Sierra Nevada and not far from the sea. My great-grandfather Pepe was from one of the first towns you find as you start to go up the mountains, called Almejíjar.

I stayed for a night in a hotel in Pampaneira, a town almost all the way to the top, where I would be working at the town hall as a mountain guide. This was the first time I was in a hotel by myself, found by me as I walked the streets. I felt independent as I entered the small room with its twin beds and bathroom. The bed covers were made of colorful mountain wool that was typical of the area and the window overlooked the street.

Before my job started I had some time to find a place to live. I went to see places to rent the next morning.

I found a house on my second day, near the trail that connects Pampaneira to Bubión, the next town up. It had two bedrooms and I took the first one, with a double bed and a huge painting of the Virgin Mary on the wall above. The living-room/dining room was spacious. Because the town was on a steep pendant, the front door faced the roof of my neighbor and the mountains. You had to be careful walking down the hill to the square, because of the pendant and the water flowing through the middle of most narrow streets. There were no sidewalks but then again no cars, just a donkey here and there. People's windows and doors were open as it was starting to get warm, and I could always hear Ricky Martin's Soccer World Cup song *Allez allez allez!* playing.

On that first day in my rented house I bought eggs from an old lady who lived next door and had to borrow a pan from another neighbor to fry them. That was the only food I knew how to cook for now. I went to the market and put my little shopping of tomatoes, lettuce, coffee, and biscuits in the big fridge, explored the cabinets and drawers, and cooked the eggs. I unpacked and made my bed. I lived here now. It was quiet. At night both the home and the bed felt too new.

During the day I usually kept my front door open, or sat at my doorstep or on my neighbor's roof and looked at the view. It had been a dream of mine to live in a forest, or on a mountain, or both, alone. Those were the images I waited for, in my head. This was different from my dream, because in the dream it was just a relief, and in real life it was all kinds of things, although in both I was escaping. I enjoyed the calm, and not being anyone's burden as I had felt back home. I could have my own rhythm. Sometimes in order to experience freedom, you have to escape. I did wish I could cook, but I had done well. A water leakage had flooded half the house during the first week, and I had sorted it out by myself with a mop and bucket. I was going to be fine.

That week I met my boss Joaquín who took me up to see Trevélez, his town at the very top. There we had tapas to try the local ham that made the town famous in Spain. We sat outside, ate a tapa of ham and bread, and had a caña, which is less than a half pint of draft beer. Joaquín was cheerful, a natural leader whom you could tell enjoyed his life and where he lived. He then took me to the tourism office at the town hall to meet Juan, a tell-it-like-it-is, no-bullshit man who looked more serious than Joaquín, and also owned a bodega next door where he had all kinds of cheese, wine, and local preserves as well as artisan decorations. I discovered an almond cheese he sold. It tasted like marzipan and became my comfort food while I lived there. Going to Juan's bodega was one of my favorite things to do. It felt like being in a Moroccan bazaar. I could sit at the small bar, have a wine, eat some olives, and talk to Juan.

I got a book from the tourism office about the history of the Alpujarras. All I remember from it now is how the Moors had rebelled against Phillip II of Spain on those mountains. I imagined the scene on one of the trails, anachronistic. They were eventually thrown away by the troops for not converting completely to catholicism, but their roots were still there, in the food, the buildings, and the people, myself included. I am a mixture of many places but my thick eyebrows and big brown eyes are mainly from my great-grandmother's family, an hour's drive south. I took a walking tour of my own town, and imagined that by the time the tourists came I would know it well.

A week later, on my first day working at the town hall they filmed a commercial to promote tourism. I appeared as the person at the front desk of the tourism office and gift shop. I thought it would be nice if that was my position, but they wanted me for the outdoors. The next day I was to go up to the mountains with Joaquín and Juan and a group of retired European mountain hikers. I was going to use my English and the French I had ended up learning at school in the summer. I was told to prepare for cold weather and wear hiking shoes. But I had looked at the mountains and they seemed like the ones near my house back home and I didn't use hiking boots for that. Nobody did. Also, it was almost summer.

I arrived at the bus in the morning to find the hikers super geared-up, with fancy hiking boots and trousers. Everyone had walking poles and looked fit and up for a serious mountain. European hikers are always so over-geared, I thought.

Once we started going up, I saw the snow. Ah, I didn't know there would be snow up here in the late spring. I now wanted some of that gear. I regretted my light running shoes and not having asked more questions. Or listened. I had heard that the Mulhacén was the tallest peak in the Iberian peninsula, but this mountain range was so near the sea I would have never imagined permanent snow.

We started walking and I made my way up to the front, as if I were leading but with no idea where I was going, so that nobody would see my face as I sank my feet into the snow, which kept getting deeper, of course. I repeatedly said I was fine but this guide had zero credibility now. I cried silently from the pain.

Once when I was little my hands had gone dark purple because I had been making a snowman for a long time and had taken my gloves off. When Carmen, who now worked at my abuela's house and had been looking after me, realized, she ran inside with me and put my hands under warm water until the blood started flowing again. I prayed my feet weren't going purple. We stopped for lunch and I took off my shoes, dreading the sight of my feet, but they were not purple, to my relief. One of the hikers offered two plastic bags to prevent them from getting wet, so I dried them, put a foot in each bag and then put my socks and shoes back on. Genius. Still cold, but maybe not deadly. The way down was easier. I decided to get the proper gear and stop assuming things from now on.

That weekend my cousin Ana and her boyfriend came to visit. It was so nice to have visitors. It still always is wherever I am. We smoked hashish, sat on my neighbor's roof looking at the mountains, and walked around town, high. Ana said my mother had been calling and asking why I had gone to the mountains alone and what I was doing there. They took a photo of me reading my tourism book sitting on the neighbor's roof to show her I was studying. I sent it with a postcard. Soon after Ana and her boyfriend had left, my aunt Charo called me from Granada. She was very worried because my mother had phoned saying that if I did not come down from the mountain she was going to get on a plane and make me come down herself. I didn't understand. What had I done now? I wasn't any trouble and was not asking for anything. I was saving money to travel. What did she want from me now?

My mother knew very well what that was. She phoned me the next day, and said,

"You did not come out of the Andes to hide in the Sierra Nevada. Why can't you just go to visit the Italian family, or go to Paris?!"

Paris? I explained I was going to travel at the end of the summer when I had saved money, so I could go to more

56

places than that. I had no intention of going to Paris yet. I was exactly where I wanted to be. But my mother wanted me to travel to a few places, preferably ones she had been in, and to visit the family she herself had visited, and then return home to go to university. Aunt Charo asked me to please return to her home in Granada because she didn't want problems with the family.

Maybe my mother was scared I would stay in Spain longer than planned, like she did. Maybe she thought I would fall in love as she had too, and stay too long, or maybe never come back. I had gone to the other end of the world and her expectations still followed me.

After hanging up the phone with my aunt Charo I put on my running shoes and ran up the hill to Bubión, the next town. I hadn't even had a chance to see it properly yet, but I ran back to the house before doing so. I just wanted to cry. I hadn't even seen my great-grandad's town Almejíjar either.

My mother had said that my family in Argentina would get me a Eurail Pass of seven journeys as an early birthday present, so that I could travel seven times and then return to Argentina. It was my parents' idea and everyone would chip in: my abuela, aunts, uncle, and Carmen. I was grateful for the gift but not the control that came with it and certainly not the ruining of my plans to live on my own, make money, and travel on my own terms. Which was going very well for once. I didn't want anything from anyone. I wanted to be independent.

The next day, the tourism office was closed. I went to Juan's bodega and sat at the bar and told him everything. I was hoping for a miracle.

"Divorce your parents." He said without any doubt that it was the solution, as he poured me a glass of wine. "I did it myself. Best decision of my life."

"How? At a consulate?" I did think about it, but I didn't want to go as far as getting a divorce. It scared me to completely remove myself from my family. I didn't want to upset them more, but maybe this was the price of freedom. Maybe being free means you upset others, and need to separate yourself, because otherwise they will not tolerate this freedom. Why would independence have to cost so much, and be so difficult?

The next morning I went to say goodbye to Joaquín at the office. I was not strong enough to divorce my parents. In a few years I would be twenty-one and in Argentina that meant I was not underage anymore. I would wait for that. Juan and Joaquín gave me a t-shirt of the Aplujarras with drawings of the flora and fauna and said that if I did decide to divorce my parents and come back, I would be welcome anytime. Then I left my first home alone and took the bus back to Granada. It had not lasted long, but soon I would live by myself again, I thought.

I took a bus back to my uncle's house. Macarena said I had to get rid of my ridiculous suitcase and turn into a backpacker. I had only just heard of those. I was still hoping to somehow stay in England instead of going back home, perhaps by working as an au pair, but I was going to backpack first and make the most of the seven train rides. We went to El Corte Inglés, the local department store, and I got a blue Altus backpack.

Macarena showed me how to fold my clothes in squares piled up and pack the sides of the backpack with shoes, shampoo, etc. I later met people who rolled their stuff, but I carried on with my folding. My cousin Enriquito gave me a pocket lock-knife to take. I got a Hostelling International book bible and I was ready.

On my last night Macarena took me out around the Albaicín and we went into a cave to a small flamenco night among friends, with just a guitar, singing, and clapping. I said to her that maybe I should at least have learned the clapping. I had done nothing productive. All I had imagined or attempted had failed or was interrupted. I was going on this trip a bit defeated and definitely not expecting much.

There was a kitten in the cave and one of the gypsies said it was mine if I wanted it. Macarena thought I should go traveling with the kitten. She saw no limits. Maybe if it had been a dog. She said I could also stay and not go traveling, and live in this neighborhood with my cat, and never tell my mother or hers where I was. I loved each of those ideas and considered them, but my uncle Paco in Madrid was waiting for me, and I was kind of already gone.

It was early June in Madrid. I took buses from uncle Paco's house into town and touristed around during the day, my favorite museum being Reina Sofía where I found Picasso and Dalí and the fact that the Spanish invented the mop and the lollipop.

That week I felt I was in danger for the first time. I took the bus from Atocha, the main train and bus station in the center, to get back to my uncle's outside of town, and missed my stop. I was on a tight budget, so I stayed on the bus at the back, until everyone got off, waiting there for the five- minute break to be over and new passengers to arrive. When the bus driver got up and walked to the back, he saw me. I explained my situation. He said it was okay and that I didn't have to exit the bus. Then he opened the back doors and unzipped his trousers. Urine started to hit the bus steps and the pavement. It was shocking, but because he looked about sixty I was not too worried. These Spanish folk seemed rude and brute to me, anyway, so I thought peeing from the door must be normal. When he finished he walked further to the back, sat right next to me, and started talking. I didn't know what to do or answer.

"What's your name?"

"Dolores."

"But you're not from here, are you?"

"I'm from Argentina. I'm here at my uncle's."

"You don't say. You're a beautiful girl."

I just wanted him to get up and leave me alone. Then he put his hand on my knee and my brain could not make sense of it. I froze for a moment until he moved his hand all the way up my thigh. I took his hand off and pushed him away with all my strength. Adrenaline flooded my body. I moved out of the seat and ran to the glass door that I could not open with the button. I started shouting and hitting it.

BAM! BAM! BAM!

"Open now!" I shouted.

BAM! BAM! BAM!

"Open, NOW!"

"Shut up", he said casually. "God, you're crazy!" He took his time standing and slowly went

to the front of the bus to open the back door.

I escaped through the urinated steps and waited out-side until people started arriving. I waited for everyone to get on the bus, then I boarded and walked straight to the back without paying. I made sure I did not miss my stop and pushed the experience to the back of my mind. But now I knew I had to be very careful if I was to backpack by myself, or be a woman alone anywhere.

Once on the overnight train to Barcelona I looked out the window as my carriage started to fill and we set off. Then I left to stand with the smokers in the part where the wagon begins, which is open, looking out until it got dark. There was marihuana, hashish, and tobacco. I had just one ciga-rette as I was not feeling very well.

The next morning I got off the train at Barcelona Sants Station and had a strawberry lollipop for breakfast while I walked and made it to the Arc de Triomf where there was a hostel.

Almost Paris, mum.

I walked to Pasaj de Gracia Street and went up the stairs. The hostel had no beds available until midday. It was 7 am, so I asked if I could wait inside as by now I was sure I had a fever. They let me wait on a chair by reception. I tried to keep sitting upright on that small wooden chair. Two friendly Mexican guys approached reception and asked if I was okay. One of them offered me Tylenol. He said he had a pharmacy with him. His father was a doctor, he told me, who sent him off prepared. I had never heard of Tylenol so he explained what it was. I took one and it worked. His name was Rodrigo, my first friend backpacking.

A few hours later a group of girls came up the stairs together, led by a Chilean girl. They looked like they were enjoying themselves. I wondered if I would end up making friends like that, or get to know those girls. Or would I spend most of my time alone? In the Alpujarras I had realized when my cousin came to visit, how sharing time with people who I can be myself with, is as necessary for me as spending time alone. I missed my friends from Argentina, although I would not trade this for anything in the world. That night I met the girls in the dining area and the next night we went partying with the Mexican guys and more people from the hostel.

I have never been too fond of clubbing. I didn't mind it here; dancing was to be part of my trip even if not flamenco like my mother. There was a Polish girl who moved in a very different way to everyone else, and nothing like I had seen in Madrid, Granada, or in Mendoza where everyone danced similarly in clubs. Unless everyone in Poland moved like her, but I didn't think so. She was so free. The place I came from had a uniformed everything, as far as I knew, or at least in the circles where I had moved. I wanted to feel that freedom. I knew I could. I was starting to.

I ended up staying in this hostel for two weeks. I was not used to the quick arriving and leaving, so typical of these trips. I had no time limit, could live on very little, and wanted to know each place well, if I liked it. My friend Rodrigo was studying film. I told him I wanted to study acting, and he shared his idea of renting a house in Paris where a crew of artists would live and make things. He said I was welcome to join them. He spoke with such enthusiasm about everything and I was glad I had retaken French. I was so up for that life.

Verónica, the Chilean, was an ex-model who had rebelled in a hotel room the night before the Miss Chile beauty pageant where she was a finalist, by eating almost a whole roasted chicken. She had to squeeze herself into her dress the next day without breathing, deciding this was the end of that life. She got through the day as she could, taking a few Pisco Sour drinks that were passed around by waiters before the taping of the live show. She would shortly be interviewed on live television, but she did not care anymore. She slurred her last words as a model and thanked God that she didn't win. Now a fashion designer who created wardrobes for rock bands, she had sold her car to travel to Europe and be inspired, after going through a break-up. She had great style. Not that I knew for sure what that was. We decided to keep in touch and meet again if we wanted to go to the same place.

On the final days of June I went to Milano in Italy to meet more family. There I found the best treasure I could have imagined. It was a "magic" pen, which a guy from the US told me about while we changed trains at the Pisa station. He said I could get one in Milano. The pen had an eraser at the end that made the ink on paper disappear just by touching it. Eurail passes had blank boxes for each day you decided to use trains, and you would fill in the date you travelled. I had five of my seven spaces left on my pass so I was going to use the next one as much as I could by erasing the date and writing another one later on that same space. My trip changed from a one-month trip to three months. Twenty-one travel days instead of the original seven. We "all" did it until the end of the summer when the ticket inspectors started catching us and punched holes on the spaces instead.

I then went to Nice by myself. After a few days Verónica

came to meet me there in my hostel. Our roommates were three Canadian girls whom we joined, going to Florence, Rome, and Greece together.

After visiting Corfu in Greece, Verónica and I went to Paris. We had been bitten by bugs all over our legs from hanging out in parks and sleeping in train stations and even a sidewalk before taking the early ferry to Corfu. I went to the doctor as I had insurance from my mother's travel agency, and Verónica and I shared the medicine. We were not in good shape when we got to Ireland. We were not eating well. Guinness for breakfast with the local old men. Kit Kats for lunch to make our money last. Nutella from the jar. Or just cheap sliced bread out of the long bag. I got ill with a fever again.

When we got to Brighton, where I was hoping to live and be an au pair, I realized I didn't feel the vibe in the town. A friend of my cousin Ana in Granada had put me in touch with an au pair company he had worked with in Brighton. But I didn't even go to the interview I had lined up.

It was so quiet in Brighton, after being in Paris. Vero and I considered staying and getting other jobs, we even called a few places we found in the newspaper, but nobody would rent us an apartment because we had tourist visas. We took a bus to London the same day.

Another hostel with shared bunk beds, but with tea and eggs or beans on toast for breakfast. At the table we met a couple from Argentina who lived at the hostel and worked as living statues in Hyde Park. I kept asking everyone what they did to earn a living, or what I could do. I liked how cosmopolitan London was. I loved all the music in the streets. Buskers in every corner. It was the end of July; the middle of summer. There was an area called Theatreland around Covent Garden, and theatres everywhere. I was impressed by how people dressed, colorful and vibrant, especially around Camden Town. Hyde Park had protests on the weekend. They were peaceful and the signs people held up were even humorous. I remember a grown man standing on a wooden box, making a speech although I cannot remember what about, near where the living statues were, which included the couple I met at the hostel.

I started looking for work. I had to find a job as there was no way I was going to leave this city. For days I walked the streets around Hyde Park, but it seemed I needed a European nationality to be able to work. I looked at apartments. There was long-term rent available. I needed a job. I could get a European passport from my Italian grandfather's father, Dino, but I would have to wait a long time for that. And the Spanish one was impossible to get.

One night I called home to report myself and my parents were furious with me again. They wanted to know where I was getting money to keep traveling. I seriously believed that my father was capable of coming to find me if I didn't go back home. I promised that at least I would start by going back to Spain. I angrily cried by the payphone outside of a Waitrose supermarket in South Kensington. I would come back to London, I thought. One way or another, one day I would live here.

I went back to Spain, first arriving at the Feria de Málaga. But after a day of partying there with Verónica I decided to go straight back to Granada. I needed a break and I missed my family there too. I was feeling down because my plan was not working, I could not find jobs to support myself and stay in Europe, and my money was dwindling. There were no buses running that day in Málaga. It was the middle of the day and I hoped for a taxi as I stood under the sun. I waited at the beginning of the highway eating my meal of the day, an apple and a can of corn, which I opened with the lock knife my cousin gave me. I didn't even tell my uncle or aunt that I was coming back. I was eighteen and not thinking about those common sense things. They found me sitting on the floor by the door of their apartment. I realized from their faces that I should have let them know.

About ten days later, Vero called the phone at my aunt's shop to tell me she was in a hostel in Madrid that was really fun and I should join her and her new friends. My Madrid family was away for the summer. I wondered if I should go back home to Argentina. It was the end of August and summer was almost over. I was running out of money and I was getting tired of being in other people's homes or in hostels, not having the same space to come back to for more than a few days. I had my open plane ticket from Madrid.

Maybe this was the time to fly home.

We stayed in that hostel in Madrid for a few weeks, until my last peseta was spent. The people were indeed too much fun. I spent my nineteenth birthday there, and the overnight receptionist let me have a party. We spent a few nights a week sleeping on a bench in Plaza de España, the nearby square, or stayed out all night between bars and clubs. This way we saved money so we could stay in Spain for longer. As trusted guests, the hostel let us keep our bags in their lockers.

Vero had a new boyfriend from the hostel, who was also from her hometown. He would be back home soon, so it was clearly the end of the trip. Vero often found boyfriends. I was not as open. I still hadn't even lost my virginity. My mind was elsewhere.

A few days after my birthday, we had lunch at a table on the sidewalk with a glass of wine, saying goodbye to Spain. Spending the last pesetas and deciding then and there that this was the end. We went straight into the travel agency across the street and booked our flights.

Vero planned our outfits for returning home. I wore a long black skirt, a white t-shirt, a grey fake suede jacket from a second-hand street market and a pair of shoes with tractor tire wedges. They smelled because I also got them secondhand and wore them for an entire month straight without socks. Vero had black crop trousers, black wedge sandals adding to her already dramatic height, a metallic silver shirt, and double hair buns like Gwen Stefani.

We found each other at the airport during our layover in Brazil. We both looked at each other and said, "What have we done?" Maybe we should have not had wine before going into the agency. Maybe I could have found an illegal job and stayed. We sat waiting for our next flight, she to Chile and I to Argentina, looking out of the windows, dreaming of seeing Sao Paulo instead. We had started something irreversible. We had both left home indefinitely with a one-way ticket and not much of a plan. We had gone to a new place and then another and so on. With everywhere we went the world became bigger and so had our curiosity for it.

Living With the Wives of God

Landing back in Argentina was surprisingly unfamiliar. My family was at the airport. My friends were there as well, with a sign that said, "Welcome Back to Reality". As if it had all been a dream and this was what they would hear when I told them about being abroad. Yet it was comforting to see them. It was also comforting to see the mountains, even from the plane before landing. Being far away showed me what I took for granted. I lived by the biggest most majestic mountains in the Andes. But Mendoza felt different. I missed being in unknown places and the feeling of adventure. How would I talk to my friends about what I had experienced? They had never left home themselves. I had changed. Everyone else had, too. I saw the city differently. Familiar although smaller than I remembered it, new Argentinian music sounding on the radio that everyone knew the lyrics to except me, there were new friends of my friends, who now went to university. Perhaps the city had also changed. Either way, it did not feel like going "back". Maybe there is no going back. Once you leave for a long time, it will never be the same.

After being out there alone and free, I was also back at my parents' home under their care and rules, thankfully not for long because I would be going to university. It was nice to relax at home, but I didn't belong there anymore.

I spoke to Verónica on the phone and she also felt strange. I took a bus to Chile for a weekend and stayed at her house in Santiago, which is only four hours away across the Andes. She was throwing a Halloween party. She dressed as a metallic galactic thing full of kitchen foil because she loved the new Beastie Boys *Intergalactic* song. I was Wednesday from the Addams Family. She had gone back with her old boyfriend. Everything was as it used to be, but it was really not for her, either.

Then I went back to Mendoza and prepared to go to Buenos Aires to sit for the exams to get into university.

I had decided on a journalism degree and a weekly theatre class, negotiating with my parents who worried I was going to end up living under a bridge if I didn't study something safe, as if journalism was safe. Also, if I changed to theatre I would have to pay for everything myself. I would be "alone" in this, and it was very difficult for a student to have a job to support themselves and study in Buenos Aires. Even if you went to the free university.

The Residency was supposed to have been the least expensive place for me to live. I later would call it El Claustro, the Cloister. Ran by the Wives of God, some kind of nuns, I understood. My mother and I had been to Buenos Aires, seeing many places for me to live, but this one had all meals included, my mother said. It also had an early curfew. My parents must have felt better having me under the care of nuns after disappearing in Europe a few times. Still, I knew I was lucky to be able to do this, to have my parents pay for a place to live and for my studies. I would be far from home and in a big city. How bad could it be. So the Claustro it was, for my first year at university.

The ladies who ran the Residency, Delia and Marisa, greeted me at the big French-style building with smiles, short hair, and very long skirts. The "Consecrated Servant Wives of God" actually marry Jesus. There is a wedding at a church, and they wear a white dress just like any other bride. Except they are alone at the altar looking ahead at their murdered groom's statue behind the priest.

These women devote their lives to serve God, but can also have normal jobs and not fully live as nuns, which originally sounded progressive to me. Marisa had been a lawyer until she started to run the Residency together with Delia. They both wore buttoned-up shirts or turtlenecks with their long, heavy skirts. I would have preferred the normal nun outfit. To me it was kind of dramatic and definitely more stylish, and I would not have to worry about matching ugly woolen clothes. Delia's hair, cut into a bob, was the longest that was allowed. I wondered if they were happy. If they found real joy in Jesus. Marisa half contained a smile sometimes. Delia smiled all the time.

The building had high ceilings and a lot of dark wood. Looking down from the top of the staircase I could see the hall that led into the first-floor living room. The ground floor was for the chapel where Jesus, their husband, lived. Delia bought him flowers every week and the wives went in to pray daily. We were welcome to as well. I looked in from the door once. The floor with the living room had another big area that was just used for studying, where male and female friends were allowed at certain hours.

Curfew was every night at 11 pm. If I was to miss the 9 pm dinner, I needed to call in advance to let the Wives know. The dining area on the top floor had a big framed poster of Pope John Paul II on the wall. My room was on that floor too.

That first night I arrived a bit late to dinner as everyone was finishing praying. I said, "Amén," and sat down. I had gotten gastroenteritis the day before leaving for Buenos Aires and the doctor had given me a diet to follow. I could only eat boiled pumpkin and potatoes. When I move to a new city I usually arrive sick, or arrive and get sick, probably from the stress of the change. This started the previous year when I arrived in Barcelona as a backpacker with a high fever.

Silvi, the Residency's cook, kindly made my meals for the next three days. She was from the north of Argentina. The Claustro girls and I would go into the kitchen to drink maté with her and listen to the details of her telenovela life. We would also dye her hair, turning her roots a reddish-brown hue, and gossip, when the Wives had gone to bed. Her talking involved lots of high-pitched screaming and laughing. She was the heart of the house, like her kitchen.

My roommate Mercedes was from Entre Ríos, a province famous for its summer carnival. She was polite with the "nuns" because her aunt belonged to the congregation, but she was not a fan. I loved her. I almost killed her once when I put out my cigarette, threw it into our trash can while she was taking a nap, and left, closing the door behind me. She burst out a few minutes later together with a big black cloud. The trash had been set on fire.

The girls and I sneaked alcohol in and stayed up in my room drinking. I started to dress up as a "proper nun" character during these nights. I wore my long black skirt and a black sweater, a white t-shirt with just my face popping out on top, and black jogging bottoms hanging from the top of my head. I had a rosary around my neck and shoelaces tied up as a belt. I started to dress the girls up as angels, prostitutes, and devils. Girls who are not allowed out while the bars are open.

Once a week I would go for dinner at my cousin Claudia's apartment in the neighborhood. No longer married, she lived with her little Brussels Griffon dog. Her home was beautiful and peaceful because that is how she was, and she always had interesting friends around. There were artists and all sorts of people I loved listening to. Many who saw life outside of the normal mold as she did. She seemed to get along with her ex-husband and they were friends. Sometimes I met boyfriends who eventually disappointed her. A lot of men did.

I came back to El Claustro a bit late after having dinner at hers one night, twenty minutes after 11 pm, and found that my phonebook was open on my desk in my bedroom. I didn't keep it there. It turned out Marisa had gone into my room, looked through all of my things and found it, calling all my Buenos Aires contacts, including my aunts, and some friends of my parents, because I had not returned before curfew.

Claudia asked my father to take me out of that place I lived in so I could have a young person's life, but my parents wanted to feel like I was being looked after, meaning controlled, after they had lost track of me a few times in Europe.

I could only come in minutes after 11 pm once a week, after my acting class, and I ran back when it finished. Sometimes I would pass a Servidora, a wife of god, who was waiting for me downstairs.

Marisa went into my room another time while I wasn't there, and took a magazine page that I had put on a wall. It was the famous photograph of John Lennon in a fetal position, next to his wife Yoko Ono. I had seen it in that month's *Rolling Stone* magazine. John Lennon was naked so Marisa took it off the wall immediately. When I arrived and my roommate told me it had been her, I took the elevator down to her room on the bottom floor near the chapel. Who did she think she was? God? She was just one of his or her imposed wives. She didn't just take it off the wall but also with her, without even leaving a note. I knocked on her door and as she opened I told her she well knew that Ar-

75

ticle Twelve of the National Constitution said that private property shall not be violated. I had learnt this thanks to my father who was a lawyer, just like Marisa.

During one of the first years of high school, I was sending little papers with messages back and forth across the classroom with a friend. The geography teacher saw us and made me give her the paper I had in my hand. She read it and sent me to the headmistress' office to get an amonestación, a reprimand, like a signature in the discipline book. At home I told my father that she had read the paper, because I suspected it was not right. I didn't say I got punished with an amonestación. There was no need. He said my teacher had just violated Article Twelve of the National Constitution. He gave me a copy, and suggested I open the book at that page and leave it on her desk before she came into class next time. I did. From that day she asked me to sit at the front of the class, at her own desk for the rest of the year, to keep a close eye on me.

Marisa said she had thrown the magazine page in the trash. I asked her to go through that trash because that paper legally belonged to me. She only pretended to look for it, and said it seemed it was no longer there. I went out of the building with one of the girls, as I needed to walk. We passed some builders on Santa Fe Street who were using hammers to break sidewalk tiles. I asked if they would let me break a few because I was upset and thought it would help to get my anger out. I promised to be careful. They let me.

I felt like I was locked inside this old dark house with rules and curfews. I started to get acne from stress. I liked the company of the girls but the uneasiness was coming out and I was smoking like a chimney. We all hung out upstairs on the floor where my room was, sitting around the dining table doing homework or chatting, drinking maté. Quite a few of the Wives of God sat with us and smoked as they did their own work, or snooped around ours.

Finally my father agreed to let me stay in his little studio apartment during weekends. He rented it for when he worked in Buenos Aires during the week. Even on a normal day it smelled like nobody's home and there were cockroaches. Sometimes one of the girls would stay with me with her parents' authorization, and we would steal some food from the Claustro's kitchen like tins of tuna and rice, or if we dared, a big tin of dulce de batata, a solid sweet potato paste you eat with cheese as dessert. This gave us a sense of independence.

My friends from university and theatre class would come over for parties and crowd the place as well as the hallway outside. I would leave it as found when I went back to El Claustro on Sunday, passing the kiosk to return the beer bottles. But I am sure the cigarette smell remained. My father put up with it for having thrown me to the nuns.

I really wanted a shoebox of my own, like my new friend Lola's studio apartment. It was the tiniest, with a single bed and barely any light, but it was hers to live in freely. Lola's family just let her be. She had a boyfriend who was twenty-something years older than her and her parents were even okay with that. They lived all the way in Patagonia and trusted her. I smoked marijuana out of her window for the first time, and when I realized what the time was, I ran back to El Claustro, arriving just before 11 pm, red-eyed and fully paranoid, praying the nuns would not see me. I went straight to my bedroom, where Mercedes laughed and told me I had better put all my marijuana-smelling clothes in a bag and hide it. I did, and hid myself inside the bed covers.

I wasn't the only one hiding. Mercedes led me one day to the top of the stairs and we looked all the way down to the first floor. Marisa was sitting, watching TV in the living room, and going into her handbag by her side to bring out a bottle of wine. Why did she have to hide wine? The girls had seen her doing this before, late at night. We felt bad for her. She shouldn't have to live like that either.

A New World

Buenos Aires and journalism school was a new world. Even though life inside El Claustro was restricted and sometimes quite dark, outside of it the city felt vibrant as it always had to me with its almost tropical air, people walking as fast as I did, Corrientes Street full of bright lights and theatres. I was enjoying the city and starting to find my place in it, but I needed more freedom. I liked journalism. I could almost see a future writing in the travel section of a paper or as some kind of correspondent, but I was restless with it as well. My weekly acting classes were the only studies I was really interested in.

My journalism classmate Pablo, who was also studying acting, told me the International Theatre Festival was happening. I had not even heard of this, with my head buried in university and the Claustro. There was a Peter Brook play from the UK that day right after class. We got out of the building and ran a few blocks towards Corrientes Street, to the Teatro San Martín, to see if we could get tickets, but they had sold out. The hall was full of well-known actors, soap opera stars, and lots of very posh people.

Nobody was re-selling tickets outside. We joined the line to go in anyway. We just felt like sticking around until we got kicked out, defeated but in denial. The line moved and was heading down a flight of stairs when an usher asked for our tickets. Without even a glance at each other we both pretended to look for them. There was an unspoken, un-reasonable perseverance going on. We would at least waste their time. The usher's patience ran out. "Do you actually *have* a ticket?" I said yes as Pablo said no. After a few seconds of silence a lady behind us said, "I have their tickets," and gave us each one, saying, "I'm from the British embassy, we brought the show here. You can sit with us."

We almost kissed her. We went in triumphantly and sat in the third row. Then we were blown away. I had only just heard of Peter Brook. The show *The Man Who* was based on the book by Oliver Sacks *The Man Who Mistook His Wife for a Hat*. It's about people who suffer from neurological conditions. The stage was almost bare. There were many elderly actors among the diverse cast. Quite a few of these performers had been with him for many years, Brook would travel the world and put a company together with people from everywhere. I had not seen this sort of company before. Each moment in the show was strong in a different way to what I had been seeing on stage. The acting was naturalistic, but not the way the story was presented. What was going on felt sometimes dream- like. It was poetic. There were cameras and screens showing very close close-ups of actors' faces, or what a character was drawing on paper. It had the British humor I already loved from films. Maybe it was the use of older actors that made it the deepest thing I had ever seen, or the strong images I could not get out of my mind, but it moved me more than any piece of theatre I had seen before.

That night I didn't want to stay in university. I wanted to go to England. Peter Brook brought back all the colors of London to me. I had wanted to stay there so badly two years earlier. Now I wanted to learn about theatre there. I was sure of it.

I was so inspired that I moved back home to Mendoza and got into the free university. While I worked to save money to go to England, I wanted to study theatre full-time.

After a year of journalism studies and living with semi-nuns, I was back from Buenos Aires and at my parents' home. If I was to study theatre at the local University of Cuyo, I was told I could sleep and eat at home but that was the end of it. My parents did not support my decision to pursue an artistic career. They would not leave me on the street, but that was it. I would endure living at home under their rules for the opportunity to save money to go where I wanted to go. Do what I longed to be doing. I just hoped that I would be able to do this as fast as possible so I could finally live on my own in London.

I worked at a tapas bar in the evenings. Some days I did door-to-door surveys in neighborhoods far away, where normally I would not be going on my own because it was not supposed to be very safe. I also got a job at a "telefónica" a place with several phone booths where people go to make their calls and then pay at the front desk. And behind the desk was a separate business, a Santeria where I sold saint stamps and saint figures and big red candles shaped as penises. I walked more than an hour to get there and to return home.

Even if saving money to leave was my priority, I did enjoy my university time. The program was a dream to me. I discovered Molière and improvisation. I was surprised that I even liked the movement class. Loved it, in fact. I had never been much of a mover, not sporty at all, but I began to look forward to it more than any of my other classes. We had a costume department with corsets and all. Still, we didn't get as much class time as I would have liked in the end as there were many strikes going on that year. I started to take part in them.

In Argentina, education is free for all. Even if you are a foreigner. You have the option to attend a private one and pay, but the public university is one of the best and where I was studying then. The government was considering reducing funds for universities, which meant a lot of students would now not be able to afford their studies. So I ended up on an overnight bus back to Buenos Aires with my classmates, to go to the bigger protests, occupying the Theatre Conservatory. Many students who had come from outside the capital city stayed overnight in their sleeping bags on classroom floors. I was staying at my cousin Claudia's at night, and would get up in the morning to join the others. Teachers came in from all over the country to give free classes and occupy the university with us.

We were taking a class with a teacher who was well-known for his avant-garde theatre. A very modern clown, he must have been in his late thirties, his hair beginning to gray. He said to all of us, from the classroom stage to the auditorium, that before breaking the mold (as he was doing), you first have to master classical styles. He presented Pablo Picasso's *Dove of Peace* as an example, explaining how the artist had first painted it the classical way. This really upset me. I didn't say anything, but who says this has to be the only way? Why would someone make a big statement like that about art? Isn't art a place where anything can be? Where we can put the usual order of things aside and explore and express in a different way. Why would art of all things have to be classical before it could be free? I liked art because it could show me something I was not expecting to see, in a way I was not expecting either. I refused to hear this.

I enjoyed his class, however, and all the classes we took with the teachers who protested with us. I met so many people. Some came to Claudia's house to take showers. She wanted to help too. The whole country was involved in the protests, and Buenos Aires was buzzing with this energy.

Apart from taking over the classrooms, students also protested outside. On the last night we went to Corrientes Street, which was always alive with its bright theatre signs, traffic, and people. We filled the streets, cutting the traffic. I was on people's shoulders a lot. There were acrobats and dancers, and our faces were painted. We triumphed and saved free education that week. We made noise and kept our rights. I had wanted to see that people can be united, and I needed to be among the ones who were on the same fight and on the same path as me.

During my university protest week I saw my chance of getting a tattoo. I wanted a tattoo on my body as a bold mark of owning who I was, and celebrating it. I had enough scars that reminded me of my survival. I knew what being marked was like, and I wanted to make my own, different marks. An expression of my spirit on my skin and a reminder to myself that I could exist without being scared of who I was.

I walked into Galería Bond Street, where you could find shops with secondhand clothes, leather jackets, punk-style jewelry. There was one tattoo studio. The reason I went in was that I knew of no other and I didn't want to bother asking or talking to anyone about it because I didn't want to discuss this. It was a very private decision for me, which emerged suddenly and I knew this was the time for it. I went inside the shop and looked through a book, searching for images of plants. I had seen a rap artist on MTV who had some shapes and plants growing from her belly upwards along her ribs, because that was where her voice came from and how it moved through her body. When I saw this I had just started singing lessons and voice lessons in university, and I could relate to the feeling of that force coming from the center of my belly. Maybe I wanted something similar in that area of my body. But then I saw a black jaguar and did not doubt it for a second. That jaguar called me and I forgot all about the plants.

"Just make it less angry," I said, something I regretted later. It was jumping with its teeth out and it wasn't angry. It was fierce. That's why I was drawn to it. But that is how I saw fierceness back then, as negative and harmful. I was afraid of it even if I had it as well. Jaguars hunt with a bite straight to the skull. I was going to need this assertiveness and strength for what was coming.

There is a fierceness in me that people see that sometimes I forget. I remember my mother driving me back from the dentist one day when I was young. The familiar ride under the shade of the trees lining the streets, which I still had not learnt because I never paid attention to the road. She was trying to tell me something in a nice way but she didn't know how. My dentist had told her that she would not be my dentist anymore, unless I changed the way I looked at her. She said the look in my eyes disturbed her and she could not work in peace.

My mother said I should control my eyes, like she knew what the dentist was talking about, but never thought that it would actually cause trouble.

How could I as a nine-year-old have such an effect on an adult lady? Part of me liked that I had upset her. She was not discreet as she put the needle in the flame to disinfect it for the anesthetic. I could not help looking at that fire. She then injected me without letting the needle cool down and without a warning, only "Abrí!"

It burned my gums and the liquid dripping out of the metal syringe numbed my tongue first. To me, she was *bruta*.

I got scared of my eyes, as she must have been. How did I look at her to make her so upset?

"I don't know. You have a strong look in your eyes, so be careful," said my mother.

My abuela said my eyes were hers. My aunt said they were hers. I tried to be mindful of how I looked at the dentist on the following visit, but when she started to heat up the needle again I knew I had to shut my eyes until the end of the appointment.

Would I continue to upset people, just by being myself? Is a woman, a girl, not supposed to have a strong look in her eyes? Must they always project sweetness? I could not control them. I could only accept them and their fierceness, and the jaguar tattoo would remind me of what I should not be afraid of, to be strong in myself regardless of how I was seen by the eyes of others.

The tattoo artist looked at me again, a small nineteen-year-old girl who had walked off the streets of Buenos Aires on a whim to be marked.

"Are you sure you don't want it on another part of the body?" said the artist. "It will hurt on the rib."

"I will be fine."

"And that you want this jaguar? Do you maybe want to think about it?"

"No, I am sure."

The needle started. It was irreversible. I was owning that strength inside me. As the wolf had called me when I was a child, the jaguar was calling now.

Crazy Jesus

My fierceness, drive and curiosity always kept me on track. I was determined to study in London even if I would have to start from zero again.

The degree prospectuses from UK universities arrived by mail. I worked on getting my Italian nationality so I could study and work in the European Union. My uncle Marco in Lombardia was helping me get my bisnonno's birth certificate, the last paper I needed.

The university where I was studying now, the *Universidad Nacional de Cuyo* in Mendoza, was at the top of San Martin Park which begins in the city center and goes all the way up to the base of a hill at the feet of the Andes. The theatre college building was brand new. It had exposed brick walls and big windows, with round columns painted in primary colors. First-year students were on the ground floor.

One day after lunch break, coming back from the cafeteria upstairs, I saw a tall, long-haired bearded guy who walked around slowly, with his eyes open wide, staring into other people's. He was wearing some white robe or sheet. A second-year student, much more at home in this place than I. Some students laughed. Some stared back. Others turned around. When he stared at me with his big eyes, I got uncomfortable and went down the stairs.

A few days later I saw him again as I passed by a classroom with a big glass door. He was in his acting class, against the door from the inside, behind a curtain. Very still and focused, waiting to make his entrance, not like the crazy Jesus I had seen earlier.

The first time we hung out I was dressed in my grandmother's long green dress, the belt tied around my head, that I later donated to the costume department. I was sitting outside on the grass with classmates and he came around to talk with us. His name was Emiliano. He had his long hair tied into a ponytail and a shirt with a black-and-white geometric 90s pattern. I had never seen his smile with perfect teeth, and he was outgoing but at the same time very sweet. My friends knew him already. They told me he was a comedian, which explained the crazy Jesus. That afternoon he gave me a ride home in his car. He told me he had lived in Buenos Aires a year before I did, then he had come back to go to this university as well. We became friends first, and were friends for a while before we were a couple.

Emiliano was my first love. When my father found out that he lived alone and was older than me, and that I was going to his apartment, he kicked me out of the house.

One hour later, my friends were picking me up in a truck. I put my backpack in the back, and was gone. I didn't move to my boyfriend's apartment because I was not ready yet and I really didn't want to make my parents angrier. I stayed at friends' homes, at my aunt's, then my grandparents', and back and forth for a year.

Emiliano had two radio shows. I started working there doing comedy characters, ever since he and his co-host asked me to call in as a lady complaining about her husband while having a fight with him. We also worked in a siesta-time news show where I would imitate the president's girlfriend, saying her lines whenever there had been a "statement". Because it was siesta time, nobody minded the random comedy in the middle of the news. Most days I was going from one station to the next in his car with the other performers.

Emiliano had work he loved in Mendoza, but after trying Buenos Aires and coming back, he did not feel settled there. He also wanted to go to a new place and be inspired out of his comfort zone. He started to study English so he could come to London with me. He had always refused to learn the language even though his mother was an English teacher and still ran an afternoon English school from her house. Or maybe as a rebellion to the school taking over, even though he inevitably learnt by inertia.

"French sounds better to me, Italian, Portuguese. Just

songs sound good in English," Emiliano would say whenever I asked him how this was even possible. Now he had a reason, and while he was learning he put on a show in a café theatre where he sang in English.

Before going to London, we planned to pass by the US, to work and save money while I waited for my Italian passport (he already had his). And we had to save money in Argentina for any of that to happen. I worked weekdays, weekends, at the tapas bar, the radio shows, and the door-to-door surveys, while I studied to finish the university year. I would sit at my aunt's dining table with my younger cousins while they did their school homework.

When Emiliano and I both had saved enough for a flight and a few weeks of living in the US, I went to say goodbye to my father. He had heard that I was leaving, even though we had not spoken for almost a year. I knocked on the heavy wooden door to his office, next door to my mother's, and went inside. As soon as he saw me he looked down at his papers. I said I had come to say goodbye. He didn't move. I gave him a kiss on the cheek. He just carried on pretending to read his documents.

I said, "Chau, papá," and left. I was surprised by his pride, and guessed he did not approve of what I was doing now either.

Saying goodbye to my grandparents was the hardest of all. I had lived with them for months during this year although now I was at my aunt's house. I was closer to them than I was to my parents. I knew I was breaking their hearts. They cried as if I was taking a boat in the 1910s to the other side of the world and would never return. My grandfather repeated to me that his dad never saw his parents again once he got on that boat in Italy. Did he forget that my mother left for Europe and returned, a few times? Maybe he knew there was a big chance that I would not come back as she had.

"Bambola, what if I never see you again?" he said.

I reassured them, saying that I would call; that the world was now smaller and I would be back soon. But seeing them cry made me question if what I was doing was worth all this. Leaving them behind to go to the other end of the world meant I would miss out on a big part of their lives, and deprive them of seeing me become an adult. I was abandoning them. And they were my refuge. I cried when I got into Emiliano's car.

I didn't know I would not see my grandparents for almost three years until I could afford a flight back. Or that my father would not speak to me for all of that time either. Yet I was with someone with whom I felt at home. This made leaving a little easier.

It was December 2001. Our first stop in the US was Hampton, Virginia, a place I had never imagined I would get to know. We had joined a Work & Travel program through an agency, which got us a work visa for six months, and found us jobs in a Pizza Hut. I waitressed and Emiliano was a dishwasher because his English needed practice, which actually happened at the dishwashing station. Everyone stopped by to chat with him.

Again, we were working together and now sharing an apartment with six Brazilians and a Peruvian guy, which felt like home while being in this cold and unfamiliar town. Two bedrooms with bunk beds, one for the girls and one for the guys. We were like a family of random lost children with lots of energy and excitement. We all got along and would take turns cooking for everyone. But there was not much we could do in the town except go to the Walmart next door and to the library to check our e-mails. We needed a car to do more. Having realized it was fairly easy to get a day job in the US, we quickly wanted to be in a bigger city.

Emiliano thought we should go to New York, or at least Washington, DC. "We can get internships in radio stations or papers," he insisted. "We both have enough experience."

I had not ever considered it. I had been helping production at the siesta-time news show. He was right. His English was better, and he was confident.

He made a few phone calls to radio stations in Washington, D.C from the library and in a few days we got internships at the Voice of America Spanish branch. We left on a Greyhound bus with a month's worth of tip money because our employers had refused to pay us for that first month, to try our luck in Washington, D.C.

When we arrived it was the middle of winter. Before our unpaid internships started we stayed in a hostel full of cockroaches, while searching through the classified ads in the newspaper for a room. We also walked the streets with our printed resumes looking for paid jobs, going into stores, restaurants, hotels. We found out that nobody was looking to share their apartment with a couple, so we pretended we were friends and got a nice big room in a two-bedroom apartment near Dupont Circle, with a very nice guy who worked nine to five in finance. I think he eventually worked out that we were a couple.

Our internship began straight after moving into the apartment. We started work before dawn every day, taking the immaculate metro when it was mostly empty at 5 am. I helped translate the Spanish branch morning news, receiving them as they rolled in through the teleprinter directly from the news agencies, and taking them to my desk where I had a gigantic dictionary. I then took the metro to my paying job at a bookstore in Georgetown. Emiliano was part of the creative team at the Spanish branch in the radio station, and had another job as a barista at a cafe. Sometimes I also worked at a pizza restaurant where I ate sundaes the size of my head, US style.

A few months later I swapped all my jobs for just one as a bookkeeper at an Italian restaurant. I was surprised someone had given me this responsibility. I even asked them if they were sure. There I could eat the most delicious dishes, anything I wanted for lunch. Seafood soup and fancy pasta, tiramisu for dessert, a big step up from the sundaes and pizzas I had been living on. I was in charge of accounts: paying wages and providers, placing orders, going to the bank.

For the first time I saw how working in an office was easier than on the floor of any shop or restaurant. It was comfortable. And for the first time in my life I was gaining quite a few kilos, something I had thought was impossible for me. The food in the US was so different from that in Argentina and Spain, but mainly I was eating the uncertainty, anxiety, and sadness of having left home the way I had left it, and this time for longer. Maybe for good.

Emiliano and I began arguing at home. We both worked endlessly and slept only a few hours each night. We were disconnected, struggling to adapt. We knew this situation was only going to last a few months until we went to the UK, but we really had no idea what was coming next. We were going onto another completely new experience, again in another country.

Two Brazilian friends from our group in Hampton, Julianna and Tiago, had now also moved to D.C. Julianna came to visit after they arrived, in February. I met her downstairs so I could smoke one of her cigarettes. I had quit, but started needing them again. Julianna, a petite dancer, was wearing her aunt's big, real, golden fur coat with shoulder pads.

"Nobody wears a coat in Florianópolis," she said, "I didn't have one".

Her aunt had insisted she take it because she was going into proper cold weather. She looked like a little eighties kid who stole her mother's coat and cigarettes. She told me that a few of the people in the work-and-travel program had gone back home already, sooner than expected. She and Tiago were not getting along. It was hard to find work right now, and his English was still very basic. They had found a room, an attic above an apartment. They had been lucky with that.

"Are you and Tiago together?" I asked.

"Well...I don't know anymore," she replied.

"Same here," I said. I didn't see her again. She and Tiago flew back home a few weeks later, each to their own city.

I decided to start cooking and eating better. I called my grandmother for a few recipes, like vegetable lentil stews and chicken in tomato sauce. I began running in the park near our apartment. Emiliano joined me and we even ran when it was snowing, around our neighborhood and Georgetown.

⋆ ⋆ ⋆

We finally left the US in April, arriving in London at dusk. I had been there two years earlier in the summer with Verónica and I had known I would live there one day. I had seen myself walking around Waterloo, in my city. I just didn't know it would happen this soon, and I thought it would feel easier.

We got off the plane and onto a train. It was cold, grey, and dark, unlike the snowy and beautiful DC. It looked more like a sad film out of the train windows. The chimneys and houses that started to appear gave me some hope, reminding me of why I liked London in the first place, of its magic. As I looked inside the windows, I thought that maybe I would be inside a home like that soon, comfortable and warm.

A new hostel in London. Breakfast with strangers. Fried eggs on toast and a strong cup of tea, all of which I looked forward to every day. London was harsher than I remembered. The damp cold went through your clothes. It was early April and I kept asking everyone, "But exactly how much colder does it get here?"

We found a flat-share with an Uruguayan journalist and a Spanish linguist who worked at the BBC, where we had tried to do another internship but did not succeed in securing one. I went back to my normal weight in London, partly because we had to save money even on food because my Italian passport had not arrived yet and I had to live on my savings. But I settled into London and this eased my anxiety a little. Before the end of our time in the US Emiliano and I had begun to reconnect, as we slowly found our place and got used to being in D.C.

I could not decide what university to go to, and as soon as my Italian passport arrived I enrolled in two: Roehampton where I did theatre and cultural studies, and Goldsmiths College, where I did theatre alone. The possibility of taking classes from other degrees, or joining two different degrees, was new to me. And I wanted to try both universities. I had to try things for myself instead of deciding by thinking, analyzing, or feeling.

I later left both universities and transferred to one that had physical theatre. It may have taken years to get there, but it was the perfect place for me. Any hour outside my studies was spent working at a a cafe and at a posh English clothing store. I exhausted myself like that throughout my twenties, to the limit of my exploration and indecision. I didn't party like other students, there was no time left.

The London Eye

I stood on top of the toilet seat, trying to see if I could spot the London Eye from the bathroom's skylight window. It was August 2002. I had been in London for more than a year now, living with Emiliano in an apartment in Wandsworth Town.

I really wished I was just a little taller so I could enjoy the view fully like he did. Only on tiptoes could I see it for two seconds. It made me feel excited to be there.

I was hiding in the bathroom. It was the only place my boyfriend would not interrupt me. I had never lived with a man before him. There he was when I woke up, and the same when I went to sleep. He was the only person who really knew me here, and I, the only one who really knew him.

When we arrived I asked him to marry me. It was very spontaneous, and I didn't have a doubt. I was deeply in love with him and just the thought of losing him scared me. I wanted us to be together forever. He said yes, and that we should do it in Venice, his grandmother's town. Just the two of us so we didn't have to wait for anyone.

But things changed before we got to Venice. Soon I had to hide to have privacy and alone time, shouting out from the bathroom that I was still plucking my eyebrows. Sometimes I did pluck them, or just sat on the closed toilet seat, or the side of the bathtub. I closed my eyes and made time. I was twenty-one and attending two universities, working two jobs, things I did to myself until I fainted at the top of the stairs at work one day.

London was different from how it looked in films or from what everyone says about it. It was supposed to be orderly, a place where everything works, where the streets are clean, and the people are honest and punctual. My main shock was not understanding the accent. The English didn't all speak like Tony Blair or Julie Andrews. Also, people were not as punctual as I had heard they were. I took everything literally. I believed all this and hoped for it. So when I saw the bus stop with Express Times posted, but the bus did not show up at those times and I was late for my first day at work in a café at 7 am, I got on and said to the driver, "You're late."

Everyone looked at me like I was insane. I was. I was probably looking for order after coming out of chaos in my home, and living the internal chaos of being in a new country.

At home there was a different battle between order and chaos. I was the one doing the cleaning because Emiliano would never see dust, and I could not touch any of his papers with comedy ideas written on them no matter where they were when I cleaned. They were scraps of paper, ripped from another paper or a napkin. I tried giving him a box for his ideas but it was used for a day. Fair enough. We had to compromise.

Emiliano started to be sad very often, as he struggled to find his own place in this new city. I was not sure if it was something that had always been there that I hadn't seen back home, or even in the US where we both had struggled, but this seemed new. I started to feel guilty, since we had left home because of me. He had a good life there. Even though he insisted that he would not go back, he had worked doing what he loved and he was so great at it, and he got along with his family. I had a father who had kicked me out of the house and had been gypsying around for a year, tired of feeling like a burden. In the UK I could work and pay for my studies without anyone's help, on the exact other end of the world, which made sense to me.

I had been so in love with Emiliano that I got my first little panic attacks thinking at night that one day one of us would die first, or we both would, and it would all end. I could not bear this thought. So I shocked myself when suddenly I began to want to be alone, and not with him. Perhaps I was not in love anymore? How could love end like that? I had been thinking for a while that it would pass, the feeling of really needing to be by myself again as I always had been before I met him. It did, but after a while it always came back. I was letting myself down.

I said to a friend, "I feel like I am too married already. I don't want this life. I am so young." Another friend stressed how hard it would be to ever find a man half as good as him again, and I agreed. He was everything I could want in someone. He was the kindest, most open-hearted and open-minded person and he had the best sense of humor even now. But the desire to be without him, without anyone at all, was stronger.

I could not cheer him up anymore. I was trying. He was trying, as he always did with everything. He had already got into a master's program in university, but he was tired. His back ached from now standing up all day at his new job selling clothes, and he missed home.

I needed support too. I hadn't seen my family for two years, or spoken to my father for over three. My mother, who would never confront him or take sides, or simply denying things, kept asking me to speak to him on the phone.

When I told Emiliano that I wanted to be single again, he said I didn't know what love really was. He was very much right. I had only begun to know it, was absolutely let down by its whims, and wanted nothing to do with it again.

The decision had taken me some time, until I could define and accept it in me that it was valid to want to be on my own. To the lone wolf in me, it was time. The change was painful. I missed the relationship even though later he was my best friend. We were the people we knew and who knew us the most, and we had agreed to always look out for each other.

Emiliano helped me move my stuff to a room at a YMCA by Fulham Station until I found a place. We lay on my single bed and hugged. He kissed me and told me I would be fine.

The room was not bad. I even had my own sink and mirror, and a desk. The next morning as I went to the shared showers I saw an old man come out with his towel wrapped around his waist, wearing flip flops. I wondered what his story was, why he was living here by himself. I always left my flip flops on as I showered. I had learnt this from friends in hostels.

Emiliano would find someone else in two minutes, which he did, always open to love. I told him he was like Romeo when the play begins. He would cry about me until the first girl passed by. That happened.

I on the other hand, didn't date for three years, trying to avoid love. When I finally did go out with someone, and when that didn't work, I went to visit my sister Maria Julia who was now living in London, and stayed there for the night. Emiliano was one of her many flatmates living upstairs but she said he was never home. We weren't such close friends by now. He didn't know I was there, and I hadn't planned going. He brought a girl home that night. We heard them having sex upstairs and covered our ears laughing. I think I tried to find it funny. They ended up getting married.

A New Language

All my life I had to be careful with my body because of the surgery I had when I was born and the ones that followed because of complications from that first surgery. I had to be very careful not to fall on my coccyx and as a kid one falls on their arse all the time. I spent many afternoons crying as a nanny or my mother applied ice while scolding me for doing what other kids did. I could not even roller skate, unless I had a cushion tied to my butt, which happened once when I was in kindergarten because I already had some vanity. I had to be so mindful that I learnt to fear moving. Skiing was okay because falling on the snow was safer, so I would often be scolded for being out of control on the slopes, not measuring my skill with my speed. I did kid's races. Standing at the top of the slope I would think, "If I could just go for it in a straight line, I would."

I needed a bit of danger. Outside of the few weeks a year we skied, sports were not for me. When I was a teenager and now better at being responsible with my body, I started roller skating again, obviously without a cushion. But that was it, and I wasn't competitive. Running around the block bored me and I had to wear glasses for tennis, which was another "no" for vanity. I hid during gym class. Until university in Mendoza I had not connected with my body, realizing how I had an instrument for expression here and I didn't think I would encounter it much again. But now I was in a room at university about to focus on physical theatre for the rest of the year, being interviewed by an administrator in the drama department.

"I have no dance experience, but I really want to dance," I said.

I cringed at myself. What an absolute liar. I needed the credits and had joined this university too late to get into the straight play, which was what I really wanted to do. Be a "serious" actor. Apart from my dread of movement, I had been a radio actor for a year in Argentina before leaving. I didn't have to move much but I could do anything. And now, this was the exact opposite of what I was used to. I thought that perhaps this was happening because I needed to reach some sort of balance as a performer, but I would have preferred a gradual change.

I got into the dance-theatre show because I lied properly, like some people do in interviews. To my surprise, we weren't given those dance steps that I dreaded to follow. We were first of all given themes. The war in Chechnya. Motherhood. Womanhood, loss. We would find our own images, from the newspaper or TV, for instance, and create our own movements from the stories we saw in them. We made our own choreography; we devised the piece together. I could remember my own movements because one would lead to the other, telling the story. I was learning a new language and could be there all day, not caring how I was doing it. I felt a sense of belonging while moving all around that big rehearsal room. I was enjoying myself as much as on the radio. I would happily stay in that theatre from 10 am till 10 pm, going through the movements again and again, making sure that I would not ruin this for the actual dancers. In this and most of our classes we were fed all the Pina Bausch, Robert Wilson, and Wooster Group we could take. We watched videos of the Wooster Group where they took LSD and approached an Arthur Miller text as the director filmed them.

For an assignment our teachers encouraged us to do the same with mushrooms and film ourselves. I loved this place. I could not get hold of mushrooms so I chose to explore the style of Wilson instead. Our group had an imaginary giant baby we bathed, then somehow I ended up being a frog. We passed the assignment with a good grade and that's when I realized how art really has no rules and everything is subjective.

But now I was learning something new.

In the Devising class we were given a smoke machine, big pieces of cloth, and space, and were told "Go in there. You have three hours to create something."

"But, but what about...from what?"

"Whatever you want to say, but use the material."

I knew nothing of this freedom. After having disagreed with that teacher back in Argentina who said that we would have to master classical ways in order to break the mold, now I was being told: "Well, here you have no mold. What will you do?"

We were given a blank page on a daily basis and we learned to use freedom.

Where I came from you could barely choose a class. Everything was compulsory, except for a few options. Here everything was a choice, so you actually had to ask yourself what you wanted. You could also change your mind. I joined film editing as I had learnt you could make money from it. I left after a week and joined the theatre devising class. There are some things your body just won't let you do.

Around that time my sister Maria José moved to London—slowly, all my siblings did—and when I came home from university she would ask me if I could teach her anything new today, like how to jump and get caught, how to fall, how to catch someone. So I practiced with her. Then I discovered a video in her digital camera, where she was dancing in the living room alone.

The day of our dance-theatre show, I didn't want to go on stage. I wanted to die.

I wanted to vomit. I wanted someone to kill me and I kept saying it out loud. I cared so much about the piece we had created, and I wanted to do it justice. Of course when I went onstage that feeling of dread disappeared, just as all fears do when you concentrate on doing the thing. Or the Theatre Elf sorts it out, as they say in Argentina.

My sister came to the show together with our other flat-mates, Ericka and Lariza, from Mexico. They arrived early to my university and I caught them in an empty classroom playing, my sister being the teacher while Ericka and Lariza were the students sitting at their desks. Emiliano also came to see the show.

I survived my first nerve-wracking stage experience, and my fear of movement had turned into a love of movement and a trust in my body that I was not used to yet. I was a physical performer. I had recognized myself as an artist on the radio, but I could express and communicate in more ways. I needed to experience more of this.

Life on the Road

After graduating from university in London in June 2006, I was exhausted from studying and working. London to me was where I learnt to brave it all, not just the weather. But I needed sun and a bit of a calmer rhythm. My brother Martín was now living here too, and had moved out of my flat and in with his new girlfriend. Maria Julia was all settled in, working as a chef and also living with a new boyfriend. Meanwhile I was feeling a strong impulse to leave my job and apartment and go somewhere different.

I spent an Ibizan summer of three hard-working months waitressing to save money. Not a day off for the entire season, but I was no longer overdrawn in my bank account and had a real tan for the first time in years. Now I could go back home for a while. So with my euros and the usual two bags I managed to shrink all my belongings into, I headed to Buenos Aires. Even before graduating, a teacher had said that being Hispanic, it would be hard to get work in London.

"You are going to have to move to Spain if you want to

pursue acting," she said. "Or at least get started there first and come back with some experience, or they will not even consider you," she added after she saw the shocked expression on my face. I felt stupid because I never had thought of it. She wanted me to know what the reality of being an actor in the UK was, and at first I got angry, but I later decided it would be easier to start back home in Argentina, and then maybe return to London with something on my resume. So back I went, with my savings from the summer, landing at my cousin Claudia's apartment.

The smell of the streets in Buenos Aires reminded me of my student years there. I was excited with possibility as I usually am when just arriving anywhere, even if I have lived in the place before. I would stay at Claudia's while I figured out what to do. As usual, she guided me with no impositions and I felt at ease with her. She was rehearsing to do a play for the first time and working on a TV show as a commentator, a jobbing actor herself, exploring new territories. I was in love with physical theatre and had no idea how to start in Buenos Aires. I also wanted to try everything else, theatre and film, but I needed to make money too.

Within a month I was in a traveling theatre company doing musical theatre and plays in English, for both kids and adults. It paid well, per show. Sometimes we did three a day. I had joined in part because the company also performed Shakespeare, something I never had the chance to do in England. But I would now rather forget what we did with the Bard's work, and I am sure they do just as bad in England anyway.

Because the plays for kids were so loud and expressive, I got rid of the shyness I still had. In my twenties, acting as a five-year-old in pigtails doing pirouettes while singing, also tested my ego no matter how good the money was here. I wanted to do dramatic, poetic theatre, and films. But I needed to do this high-energy stuff first, and jump to Iggy Pop's music in the dressing room before going onstage.

I shared an apartment with my sister María José again, who was now back and working as a filmmaker in Buenos Aires. It belonged to our aunt Silvia who was kind not to raise the rent on us every month like landlords were doing due to inflation. This apartment had once belonged to our late French great-great-aunt Madeleine, once a single woman who lived alone in a boat on the Seine in Paris, and who came to Argentina after the war in search of a better life, as her sister had done. She had sold the boat, bought this apartment, and lived in it alone. She had brought all her furniture with her on a boat to Argentina, which to me sounded absolutely crazy, and everyday I imagined the table and chairs and sofa's previous lives.

I would think to myself, "I am sitting on Madeleine's wooden sofa bed, and this sofa was in a boat, in the Seine River in Paris, in the thirties. It really was there and now it is here in Buenos Aires and I am on it."

I wanted to know who sat and slept on the sofa, and had there been a party around or on it. I wanted to go back in time. I imagined Madeleine as a tall, strong-bodied woman, always wearing a hat.

My sister and I left the apartment alone often. María José

111

worked as a first assistant director, most of the time on location, and I toured Argentina and Latin America with the theatre company. We were both gone for weeks at a time, which meant our apartment would inevitably be taken over by cockroaches by the time we returned, because nobody would have changed the anti-roach tablet under the sink.

When we both met there we would do our laundry, kill roaches, sleep for days, and try to cook real food. In the winter we made lentil soup, our specialty. It was like our grandmother's, minus the chorizo. Sometimes I went to my aunt Silvia's house to visit her and my cousins and made food for everyone. I enjoyed cooking in her house because it was a *mother's* house. Although she hated the kitchen, she had good knives and utensils from her late husband who loved cooking, even if he had now been gone for many years. I made my abuela's chicken once and another time my lentil soup. Silvia watched while I chopped vegetables, the part I enjoyed the most.

"You cut the vegetables just like my husband did, in perfect squares!"

Then I would go back to petrol station yogurt and biscuits, or if we were lucky, some pasta from a restaurant in the middle of a long road to another province, which usually was very good. Homemade bread and wine, when you have been sitting in a van for hours, is luxurious to say the least. Traveling around the country meant one day we were near the jungle in the north, then two days later in Patagonia where it was freezing, then crossing to Chile. I loved traveling in that van carrying just hand luggage, even if we had no seat belts, and were sleeping in cheap hotels in the most random towns.

At the end of 2008 we got to spend two months touring around Mexico. I came back with a love for the country and a love for a man from there. My sister and I already knew him. He was Félix from London whom mutual friends had warned me not to date back in 2004 when we lived around the corner from each other.

Now in Mexico City, however, they had not been around. So Félix came to visit me in Buenos Aires a month later. He stayed for more than a month, which my sister didn't love, and we decided to move back to London together. I had auditioned for a feature film. I was penciled in but around filming time it looked like the production was not going to happen, so I moved to London first. Félix would arrive soon after he sorted out his visa. But two weeks after I had arrived in London, when I had a big room for the two of us, and a job in a clothing store, the film did happen and I returned to Argentina, to Claudia's apartment, for my first role in front of the camera.

On my first day I was so nervous that I thought I was going to ruin it for everyone. It was an international production and the hair designer, who came from Granada in Spain, was coincidentally a friend of my aunt Charo's. He told me to sit down and wait while he removed a wig from a very experienced old actress next to me. I tried not to look straight at her in the mirror when I realized who she was.

"How did it go?" He asked her.

"I was so nervous!"

I could have stayed in Buenos Aires this time after I finished my scenes, but I had promised Félix I would go to London. He was worried that I would get more work in Buenos Aires and leave him all of a sudden. I wanted him to understand that I would not. My fellow actors in the film were mainly men, and they all said to me that I was very silly to go back to London with a boyfriend who was still in Mexico. They said he surely had other girls there and that I should break up with him and stay in Buenos Aires, or go to the US. I returned to London, ignoring them.

Félix Skyped me three days before he was supposed to arrive, saying he had instead decided to move to Madrid and that he had found us a home there. He didn't ask or talk about the fact that he was changing our plans. He just informed me. I ended up in London alone again, doing a Christmas play, playing a 1950s housewife.

I stayed in London for almost six years after this. Perhaps I was trying to make it worthwhile that I had moved there again, slowly accepting that I had moved for love and it all went wrong. Even if I could turn around and return to Argentina, I had already left Buenos Aires, made a decision, and closed a chapter. Then again London had always called me back. It felt good to arrive there. I had felt excitement since landing, walking around Clapham and Battersea, finding familiar places, smells and ways. Discovering that I moved as a fish in water there and recognizing it as my home, a place where I had created a life for myself and that would always be there for me. I had planted a root and this root had drawn me there again.

I felt I had to give London time and persevere. I looked for auditions while I worked as a temp on cosmetics stands even though I was awful at applying makeup, but I tried to learn. I also tried a business selling handmade piñatas, which failed. I knew how to work hard. Then I remembered my work with Emiliano at the radio shows, how much fun it was, and how I even ended up getting paid. He had given me a few audio samples from the shows a while ago, suggesting that I should work in voiceover in London. He insisted that I could do it. I began to record demos, spending all my pennies on them and sending them to agencies. I started working as a voice actor very slowly.

I remained single for a long time again. It took me a while to mourn my relationship with Félix, something I condemned myself for but this was the way I felt things. I got along with solitude even though loneliness crept in, but I longed to share with someone in a deep way. I had a few brief relationships afterwards, but it would be six years until I found a person and I fell in love. The love that makes you feel like you're at home with someone. That you belong together. For me it came in the form of a Scotsman in a London pub by the Thames River.

The Crashing

Following and Crashing

Day 1 - Friday

I am sitting on a plane to Florence alone after I swore I would stay in LA for many months as I will go to hell for my carbon footprint. But here I am in this familiar place in the air, three weeks after returning from Argentina.

During this past year I have waited and waited. Saying he is still not moving to LA but that he will, soon. He was not ready to commit but also not to let go. And neither am I, judging from where I am sitting. I believed him every week when he said he was coming to see me and then...he didn't show up. How could I have once been so connected to someone and then suddenly so left out from what he was feeling or what was going on in his mind?

Five years ago when I met Thomas, the Scotsman, in a pub by the Thames River in London, we were both already tired of living in the city. Thomas after four years, me after fifteen, on and off. I had met him through my Polish friend Joanna, whom I had lived with years ago. Who had once made me love vodka and drink it like I never imagined I would. She was now pregnant and enjoying her last days of going out with a huge belly, no vodka for either of us at the pub by the river. Time had gone by. She had moved to Australia for her husband's work. Now they were both back and we were out with his work friends, one of which was Thomas. It was sunny and we were at the tables outside by the water, half of Wandsworth cheerfully crammed into the space under the sun.

Joanna teased, "Look at all these men. Lots of men, Doli, look."

"Yes, I see all the men and I won't stay long," I said, holding my half-pint. "I have a Skype call with the immigration lawyer in LA tonight."

I had come out of a dead-end long-distance relationship some months before and I was feeling good again on my own. After that guy thought it was a bad idea for my acting career to live on a mountain between Spain and France with him and discouraged me, saying he would feel guilty if later I regretted it. I wanted to take this opportunity of a broken heart that snapped me back to reality to finally focus on my plans. I didn't want to end up married or pregnant like my friends all seemed to be doing, not before I left London and went to live in Los Angeles, something I had dreamt of for a long time. And had almost forgotten while dating the man on the mountain.

Now I had a plan of action, which was beginning to be real even if it could take any time between a few months to even years to be realized. I would avoid any reason to stay in London any longer, including dating, especially long-term relationship material men, because what if it happened again that I wanted to leave it all for love. At the same time I dreaded my usual eternal single season between boyfriends. I have never been able to jump from one relationship to the next. I instead want to be alone after a breakup, for too long, in my opinion. I already knew I would be okay by myself, but I did miss that kind of connection even if I was contradicting myself. London could be a lonely place, like any big city.

Joanna told me I was being ridiculous and that I should have fun. "Look at me, I have vitaminosis. It's what you get from eating too healthy and not drinking enough!"

There were in fact many men in that pub. Some I knew already, and some I had never met, like Thomas. I hadn't noticed him until he spoke to me when I was standing by his table. He asked where I was from and said he was about to start Spanish lessons. We only spoke briefly. He had that charming Highland accent and sense of humor, and bright blue eyes. He also seemed younger than me, and anyway my focus was somewhere else. I left on my bicycle before the sun went down, back to Battersea, so I would be sober and on time for my Skype call.

A few days after that evening, Joanna told me that Thomas had asked for my number, which she just gave him without consulting me. I felt I had to go on a date. Just one, because actually he had seemed perfectly nice. I didn't have much experience dating British men. Maybe they just didn't like me, or I never really got them. The guys I met when I was out always seemed too reserved for my initial shyness and then suddenly too drunk for my very slow drinking. Whatever it was, I had not adapted to the cultural difference, and London being so cosmopolitan meant I could get away with it. But he was different.

We went to a pub near my office temp job on our first date. I was now working as admin support in an engineering company, where I mainly supported the admin of the CEO's mother, a ninety-two year-old expressionist painter with genius and talent to keep me inspired and a temper to make me dread my office job at the same time.

Thomas was an engineer from another company. I prepared myself to never see him again and tell my friend that I had gone on that date so now she could leave me alone. But as soon as I met him I was seduced by his confidence and calm demeanor. Something that I definitely had less of. He was very tall but carried himself with total ownership of his body and any place he entered. He was not cold as I thought he might be. He was easy to talk to and warm instead.

It was springtime and we lived in neighborhoods nearby, so we often rode bikes to see each other during the week or went on a long cycling trip together on the weekend. We were in the same rhythm. He always seemed sure about me, and I tried to take it slow and get to know him well before I fell for him but that never works if I'm going to fall for someone.

By the end of the summer I told him I wanted to make the move to LA. I wanted him to know this as soon as I knew it could actually happen that I could get my artist visa. I was nervous and scared and ready to hear him say that it was over now, but he surprised me. He said he also wanted to live abroad, which he already had done in the past when he had lived in France, and that he was up for moving to LA with me. I felt a huge relief. He asked if we could live in Madrid first for a year, so he could learn Spanish. Then we would move to California together.

I said yes, living in my Spanish language again sounded good to me. I was ready to go back to Spain as London felt like a closed chapter. I could feel the cycle of my time there ending. It had lasted a very long time.

Within a year we were living in Lavapiés, the bohemian neighborhood of Madrid.

When she saw that we were serious, Joanna said to me in her usual bossy but jokey way, "You better be nice to him."

Was this because she liked him so much that she didn't want me to lose him? Why did she not assume that I would?

His work colleagues also joked, "If you are not nice to him, we will kill you," which I took as a statement of how much they loved him. But one of them hinted to me that he had gone through a tough breakup before.

When we got to Madrid one of my cousins who lived there met him and said to me, "Doli, he is a good one. Look after him."

What was that about? How did all these people who told me to look after him perceive me? Aren't we supposed to look after each other? After the relationship? Did my cousin mean as in to "keep him?" Maybe she meant something else I didn't understand. She usually packed her boyfriend's bags every time he went away. She also made him breakfast every day at 7 am. I even tried that once, now scared that I was very possibly not looking after him, whatever this meant. He usually got up earlier than me in Madrid as he had arrived with a transfer from work straight into the new office while I stumbled into beginning again. So I decided one day I would get up with him and make breakfast before he left. Like a good girlfriend. I would do this from now on.

He just said, "You know I cannot drink coffee or eat so early."

Looking after each other is not about that sort of thing. I knew what it really meant. We were already doing that.

Moving to Madrid turned out to be a difficult transition for me even though I thought speaking Spanish would make it a breeze. The contrast with London was shocking. The pace was much slower, it was not as multicultural, and I did not realize how much I had identified with London for all those years until I arrived in Madrid. I had spent so much time in Spain, but that was long ago. I had become an adult in London. I had been free to grow into myself there. Being out of it and into the slow motion of Madrid felt like a part of my identity had been suddenly erased. I felt strange. Out of place. During our first months I would stand on the balcony looking down at our street in Lavapiés, feeling empty as if I had not fully arrived. I didn't know who I was outside of London.

I knew that starting over in a new city was not easy and that I had to get used to a new working order, so I decided to be patient with myself. I would fully transition into this new place, sooner or later.

During our first year of living together in Madrid, Thomas and I became very close. We enjoyed discovering its street life together, the bars, fun weekend markets, flamenco in our neighborhood, and short trips we took around Spain.

I played the housewife of our rented apartment for a while, mainly because I felt bad that I was not finding a day job while I struggled to get auditions in a city where I had never been an actor yet. I had some acting and voice work in London, but I was scared it would stop coming. I wanted to create work where I was. I walked the streets trying to get a job in a store, my tried and tested way of having stability. I sent resumes to every agency to get a day-job and was met with questions about my age and whether I would leave if I got an acting job. Sometimes I went to an audition, then came home to clean, tidy-up, go to the supermarket, hang clothes in the dryer, make dinner.

I did some acting mainly in commercials, but it seemed that it would take a few years for me to get momentum, and I was about to leave anyway, or so I thought. My eyes were on LA and so my two feet were not fully on the ground of Madrid. It was not even easy to make friends in this city, unlike every other place I had lived in. I began to think I was unconsciously closing up.

After a year I was depressed. I felt like going back to London or anywhere else until my artist visa for the US was approved. But I stayed in Madrid because this was our plan and I would do my part. I would compromise for love. Meanwhile, Madrid had started to become Thomas's home, even if I felt it was kicking me out.

When I took him back home to Argentina for Christmas, after my father refused to talk to him, claiming he spoke no English and me ordering him to make an effort, the night ended with my father speaking to Thomas in fluent English.

Then in Spanish he said to me, "How good is this man! Please look after him."

Jesus Christ, what is it with looking after him! Was I not doing that? Was that my role? Did they think I would not?

My mother took it to another level, saying, "I hope you will know how to look after him."

I didn't know what to reply. What did she mean? What was I missing here?

On that same trip a few days later, we met my cousins from my father's side, who are older than me, and went out for drinks with my brother and sisters. Everyone, *again*, was telling me how lucky I was. I get that Thomas is charming and adorable, as my friends had said. He hugs everyone. His laugh is deep and creases his entire face and takes over his body and you just want to be around him.

But they repeated how lucky I was so much that I started to feel uneasy. On and on they went.

Except for my cousin Javier, the eldest of the men. In front of the rest of the now drunk cousins, on the sidewalk across from the bar, he stood tall and said, "What's wrong with you all?"

He got right in front of Thomas and put his hand on his chest. "I don't know what is up with them, but the woman you are with is not easy to find. And *you* are very lucky." He lightly and not so lightly punched his chest. "I do feel you have a good heart, so for now, you are okay."

Then he looked at me and said in Spanish, "But keep an eye on him. And look after yourself."

The man who lived on the mountain whom I dated for a year, sincerely told me that he just wanted someone to always follow him. He traveled the world doing extreme sports in nature and we saw each other in-between. I once joined him for a scuba diving trip. After a year, something had to change because the long-term long-distance relationship was stressful already, and it was never the plan. So we had the conversation.

"I want a companion," he said. "Someone who will sit next to me in the passenger seat of the car when I travel. I don't want to drive alone."

First I thought it was great because I hate driving and love road trips. Then I saw myself as a little dog, curly and white with a long fringe, sitting in the passenger's seat, forever.

"You sound like you want a pet," I said.

I had always wanted to live on a mountain or in a forest, and when I visited him on his mountain, I got a bit of that life I so loved. When he came to see me, he got the city life he also loved. The live music and people. When we parted ways, he thought he should be reasonable and look for someone who could follow him, he said.

The night before that, I dreamt that he had disappeared into a million pieces, going in circles like the Skype dots that appear on the computer screen when it is trying to connect. I am still traumatized by Skype. Too many times I have been in a relationship with someone who either travels like me or lives abroad like me. I guess we inevitably find each other. Trying to hold on to those relationships, all the failed attempts at communication, meant that the music that sounds when the Skype is either calling me or calling out stirs my stomach. The man on the mountain expressed how he really wanted to live his life. It must be hard to find a person who wants to follow someone and travel constantly. For me it's something else. Being able to be accepted as me without having to follow tradition and rules. I just wanted to love and to be loved in return. I thought I had that with Thomas but maybe we saw things very differently.

Will you have me like this?

"You know I'll marry you one day," Thomas said to me while we were having dinner at my home in Battersea. We had been dating for less than a year. I got nervous. I had never dreamt of getting married and believed I didn't need that in my life. I was slightly afraid of expressing this to him, but now that he mentioned it, I liked that he had the thought of marriage with me even if just as a thought, and I was in love. But the way he said it, it seemed it would be something I would wait for and was up to him. Something he would do to me that I would be grateful for.

Sitting on a newly purchased couch in our Madrid apartment a year later, he mentioned it again. "We'll have a wedding back home. A big party with bagpipes, all of it."

"Back home, your home?" I said.

"Yeah."

"Just so you know, I don't need a wedding."

Silence.

"I don't love them," I said. "I don't even like going to weddings unless it's a close friend's.

They make me nervous. The white dress. The planning. The stress. People can just get a blessing now, you know."

"Oh, come on. Wouldn't you want a wedding with all our friends, our families?"

The thought of promising something that I really don't know how it will go, before a minister and a lot of people whose business it is not, and having to say hello to everyone for the entire night, made me nervous too.

I loved him. I wanted him to be happy, and I did believe in celebrating the union of souls. So I thought that if my doctor friend Malena medicated me the night before so I could sleep, then gave me another pill during the day so I could get through it, I could do this one day. *A wedding.*

"I never thought about it before," I said. "I just want the commitment, the union, to be our own family. But if it's not a big fuss wedding, I think I would like to, actually."

He agreed. He totally agreed with me.

Not long after that, he brought up marriage again for the third time. We had been together three years.

"Do you think one day you'd like to get married? Have a Highland wedding? That would be fun, wouldn't it?"

I kissed him and said I would love to be married to him one day. I now pictured myself in this no-fuss wedding with our close friends and family. Even if probably medicated, I began to like the picture. I was definitely ready for the commitment it meant to him. I already felt that union with him but maybe he needed the ritual.

At this moment I was starting to work as an actress in Madrid, very slowly doing more and more commercials, still waiting for auditions for anything else, traveling back to London to work. Still waiting for my artist visa for the US, one foot here and one there, one arm spread wide out.

Most of Thomas's friends back home in Scotland were now getting engaged and posting pictures on social media of the couple in usually a scenic place in nature where they'd gone for a walk, the ring popping bigger and bigger as you swiped through the photos. Some hands were manicured, some, caught by surprise, were not. I joked that I was always losing my rings and everything, so I would probably panic about losing something like that all the time. I found those posted proposals so overwhelming, the man popping this question to a woman who has been waiting, or not expecting it at all, or pretending not to be expecting it at all.

In my culture, deciding to get married is an intimate thing. We don't do big expensive rings. Maybe because there is a lot of real poverty in my country, most of us don't have them and if we do, we don't show off that kind of jewelry. The couple agrees to marry usually without the down-on-one-knee and the woman rushing to show everyone a ring. I cannot remember any of my married friends' engagement rings. I know for sure only a few of them had one. I asked my mother if she had an engagement ring and she answered "Mijita, no, how old-fashioned!"

"It's not that I don't like a man giving a woman a ring," I told Thomas. "But the power the man has here, things happening when he declares he is ready, and the impotence of the woman, and then flashing the ring for the world to see, it makes me uncomfortable somehow."

He agreed with me.

My Argentinian friend Solange shouted, "Yes!" before her fiancé had finished asking the question because dear God, when the fuck was he going to propose? She has spent too much time in England.

Soon Thomas let me know that *when* we got married I would change my name. I would be one of his clan.

I said, "In Argentina we keep our last name, and have the option to give our children both names. I like my last name. I'd like to keep it."

He almost could not believe I said this.

"I could add yours after mine!"

He still looked upset.

"I could get a British passport with just your last name?"

He got up and went to stand on the balcony. Was I supposed to shout "yes" here too? His disapproval made me feel like I was not enough for him now. I wanted to be a family with him, but why was changing my name so important? I didn't think it was fair to be expected to change it.

"Okay, I could do it I guess if I keep my name on just my Argentine passport and change it to yours on my Italian and British ones?" I tried. Luckily, I had multiple passports for multiple identities.

No, still no good.

Why can't I just go along with it all? I thought. Was there

something wrong with me? And why couldn't we reach a happy medium, find a common ground because we love each other truly. Maybe this would be part of growing up? Shedding skin and leaving myself somehow to become part of something with him?

Then came his cousin's wedding.

They planned it for three years. Everyone talked about it for three years. I don't even live in the same country and I almost knew by heart how the famous fairytale wedding would go. The bride kept posting updates on social media. Her devotion to her wedding was big.

We all traveled to a beautiful seaside town in the west of Scotland in the summer. Thomas and I arrived from Spain. The bride had her always-dreamt-of Disney Princess dress and her dad let us know all about its three-year-long creation in his speech. Big, fluffy, sparkly, the skirt folded at the front just like Cinderella's. She wore a princess crown on her head. I really wish I could remember the shoes but I always miss the shoes. She looked beautiful and seemed happy so I felt happy for her and I bought it. It was a fun wedding.

I exchanged my heels for my ankle boots halfway through the party because Scottish dancing is not for heels. I had to look for pins for my dress and fix it because the straps were loose and this traditional dancing had already made me lose my favorite earrings. This time I was scared I was going to lose my dress. I saw lots of underwear beneath kilts from old men who now are allowed to use it for their dignity. I love that they dance so wild. Saw a few arses. I was alone for a lot of this party, my boyfriend going off to talk to so many people he had not seen for a long time. There were hundreds of them, so I was alone making small talk at the table until the dancing began.

"Do you see yourself living in the Isle of Skye?" a friend of Thomas' grandmother from Skye asked me.

"No, but I love to visit."

"Because your boy was raised the highland way, you know."

By this point, everyone was drunk. I wanted to leave. My boyfriend's father was smashed and insisted I dance with him. He was drenched in sweat, like out of a pool. His mum was trying to go home and could not get her husband or any of her sons to leave and they were all falling asleep at the table. I looked at her for help but she had given up and just looked sleepily at the dance floor with an elbow on the table, her hand holding her head. I prayed this man had underwear on too because his dance moves were mad. He did. We danced and sweat flew out from his shirt.

Throughout the entire wedding, the princess bride and groom never seemed to be in the same place at the same time. Or more than a second at one place. They ran around endlessly. About three months later, they separated. She had met someone and fallen in love.

The End.

Back in Madrid, I found out my visa to the US had been approved. It was time for us to leave. Thomas had started to tell his bosses that he wanted a transfer to the US. It was around this time that he started to come home in the middle of the night drunk after saying he would have dinner with me.

My friend Joanna said to me, "You'll see, when you guys get married that will change. He'll stop drinking and stop disappearing when you have kids, you'll see."

I still was not sure if I wanted to have kids. I had been told by friends, and by my psychologist, that I had to make a decision at some point, but I could not. I wanted to be inspired to have them with whom I loved, and I was not right now, so how could I decide.

His transfer to LA wasn't happening, but the engineering company offered him a temporary transfer to Italy. I offered for him to come with me. I could support him until he found work. It took me years and a lot of stress to get my two-year visa. He took this as a joke. So I moved by myself while he went to work in Italy until his position in LA was arranged.

Crossing the Bridge

I arrived in Los Angeles into an Airbnb hosted by Ángela, a Chilean lady who had moved there in the seventies and knew the city well.

She helped me look for an apartment, guiding me with the online sites and taking me in her car to see different areas. She showed me Silver Lake where she had lived before it was gentrified although it was already cool, and where she would be now if she was in my situation.

But apartments there were ridiculously expensive and tiny, so I kept looking. I knew what I wanted. I needed light, character, doors and walls that were not falling apart, and some quiet.

I also looked in many other areas, until I settled for an old building in the middle of the city. The middle made sense because I did not know yet what my life would end-up being like, what areas I would move around. It was the old Hollywood area, a 1930s historic building that once belonged to Paramount Studios although I did not know much about it.

I loved its art deco style, the beautiful high ceilings, and garden with a pool, although in Los Angeles you cannot escape hearing some traffic. When I finally moved to my studio apartment I made sure that when I arrived a mattress would be waiting for me. I read reviews and researched the best in the market. I wanted my landing in this new place, which I had wanted to be in for so long, to be soft. To feel my home was a place where I could rest. The mattress arrived hours before I did. The building manager gave me the news as I came to her office.

I was about to turn forty, an important moment in any woman's life, and maybe because I was exactly where I wanted to be, I felt like settling down, at least for a while. While I was here, I was going to be here fully. I had always kept my belongings to a bare minimum, ready to leave without much notice or complications, even in London where I stayed for many years.

I had dreamt of Los Angeles and when I moved into my apartment it felt like my dream. A fresh start, where I would make a home while I waited for Thomas to arrive. Then maybe we would move somewhere bigger or to a house, and have a real home together.

I got a side lamp, which I picked carefully like all my plates and kitchenware. Succulents for the shelves in the kitchen. Two bigger plants in nice pots for the rest of the place. I swapped three sofas until I found the right one, a vintage 1950s sofa from the Rose Bowl flea market. I bought the same Ikea table we had in Madrid. Two comfortable 1960s-style chairs. I got anything I would need: A small vacuum cleaner; a steamer for clothes; a good hair dryer, straighteners, curlers and clothes for auditions; a rug; bookshelves for my very few books and frames for the three pictures I had. Thomas had kept the two others. The place was still minimalistic. It felt light, luminous, comfortable, and I loved everything in it. When friends came they always said how peaceful and bright it was. It was the beginning of my dream.

Or was it the end. I still didn't know.

After five months of being in LA, I traveled to Florence, Italy, to visit Thomas. He had come to California once since I'd moved and we went on a road trip to Big Sur. It was now the summer of 2019, and I was going to him.

In Florence he took me to all his favorite spots. He knew the city well already, although I could feel the loneliness he had discovered it with. We went for an aperitivo one afternoon, and on the way to the terrace we stopped by the bridge after crossing away from his neighborhood. We sat on a bench looking at the river.

"Listen, I know I can be an asshole. But I will change," he said. "Do you think we'll get married, and have a Highland wedding?"

I panicked for a second, because we had not been getting along long-distance and this question felt like it was from a place far away.

"Wait... are you proposing?"

"No, we're just talking."

I checked once more with him. "Do we have to have a wedding? I'll do it if it is what you want. I do want to spend my life with you."

He seemed pleased. The mosquitoes from the river were eating us alive so we stood up and left. I thought we were in a good place but he started to walk two feet ahead of me.

Two weeks after that in September, he stood me up in LA on my fortieth birthday. He suddenly could not fly. He stood me up every week for another month, saying he would arrive on Monday or Friday then not show up.

Finally I said I didn't want to hear from him until there was a flight or the truth about what was going on.

When Thomas did arrive in Los Angeles in November we first connected easily again. Maybe there was still love between us. But I knew there was so much now that I did not know about him, and so much he was not saying. He would drive off at 4 am every day, returning around midday, saying he did not want to wake me up because I am a light sleeper and would be in a bad mood. For ten days he went to sleep early while I lay awake, not wanting to adapt to my time zone.

I asked if he had met someone else. He said there was nobody and that he wanted to stay with me, that he was sure, and he would move here soon. He kept a phone in his rented car. I didn't understand why he was being so mysterious and knew there was something he was struggling to say. Whatever it was, he wasn't ready to make the move to another continent with me.

After a week, he went into his car again to have a "work meeting," and came back saying he suddenly had to fly back to Europe and that it was not a good idea for me to go with him.

After six weeks of failed attempts at trying to see each other, where I had tried to fly to meet him and he asked me to wait another month, I knew that there was someone else or a lie just as big. I had no proof. I had not looked for it either. There was no need. One morning I woke up and decided I did not want to live with this constant anxiety and sadness. I felt like I was losing my mind.

Before going to work, I called him in Italy and told him that I loved him but I needed honesty, and I ended the relationship. He was surprised and upset; he knew I was serious. But he did not argue and was not ready to tell me what was going on either.

When I asked him, months later, why things had changed after the conversation about the wedding on the bridge he said, "Any girl who really wants me would have just said yes."

Waiting

On my layover to Florence, I look at my phone. January 2020, two months since we have seen each other. One month since I broke up with him. I wonder what Thomas's reply will be, whether I will just spend some time in Italy by myself making some kind of closure in my head. Whether he will want to see me at all. Will he be upset that I am doing this? Will he be happy that I am on my way? I wanted to see his face; to know what had been going on, which at a distance he had not been able to tell me. I still wanted the truth. Maybe we could fix the broken communication. There were a few days when he said come to Italy, then don't come to Italy, and back and forth during which I had booked this flight. He told me he had just met a girl. Maybe we would say goodbye in person, honoring the time we spent together.

There are two missed calls. Then a text: He is in Poland, at his best friend's Stag-do. He's not even here. I phone him back. He asks why didn't I ask for his apartment keys to be left somewhere for me, and I remind him that he said I should not come, when we spoke a few days earlier.

I know I will be in Italy alone, then, for some time. I tell him it's fine. I can wait. I sigh, more waiting. The answer is always to wait.

I land in Florence. It's Friday night. Am I here for nothing now, just looking at what could have been?

I arrive at the door of Pensione Annalena in Via Romana. I open the big old doors that lead to an outdoor hall with high, high ceilings. I notice a little door to the right and a single step beneath. I am instantly back on my trip to Florence in the 1990s, where I did the dutiful tourist thing with Verónica from Chile and the Canadian girls. But all I can remember is David's backside perfectly sculpted by Michelangelo, and gelato on the bridge. This door looks exactly like our hostel door, in the same open hallway. We would hang out outside and sit on the floor at either side of it to be in the shade. I am now only a short walk down the street to the river and Ponte Vecchio, the ancient bridge.

I look ahead down the hallway to a sign pointing to my hotel. It is up a big, wide flight of concrete stairs to the right. I pass yet another big hall upstairs that has been filled with plants, sculptures, and paintings, and then get to the hotel. Everything is old and the furniture in my room reminds me of my aunt and uncle's apartment in Milano. Dino, my

141

grandfather's cousin and his wife Pina whom I visited on that trip in 1998. That was when I realized what it really meant when my grandfather would tell me that I was also Italian.

I recently found out from a DNA test that my Italian blood is from this area, Tuscany, and I am looking at it differently now. Were any of my ancestors taking part in picking up the stones of the destroyed Ponte Vecchio from under the water, to build it back up again with their fellow citizens? What part of me is waking up just by being here?

I sit in my hotel room now, looking out the window and back into my life, traversing the small signs of distance in my memories with five days to myself. It is too cold to go outside and I am tired. My mind is tired. My heart is tired. I don't feel like going out to get dinner either. I gather a bag of nuts and dried fruit, and pretzels from the plane. Thomas said he would call later but he has not, and I am not surprised.

The windows in the room look out at the neighbors' windows on old yellow walls. The blinds are heavy and it is exactly like Thomas's apartment on the touristy side across the river that I visited six months ago in the summer of 2019 when we could hear an opera singer practicing in the evening. We would arrive back at night, open the windows to let the air in, and stay looking out for a while, listening to her beautiful voice. Back then I had love and now I have silence.

Venus, the Goddess of Love
Day 2 - Saturday

The next morning I am excited to be alone in this city for a while. I want to be inspired. Perhaps because this would be the opposite of disappointed or depressed, my latest most felt.

The night before I left LA to come here, I watched a documentary about the Renaissance. I could not stop thinking about its philosophy, the realization that we can stand on our own two feet, live for nobody's dogma, and have the power to pave our own paths. These people made way for me to follow myself. I wanted to reunite with the Renaissance woman in me. I have felt guilty that I am not more moldable, more adaptable to other perspectives that don't change. My trying is maybe another reason why I wanted to come. But now I am discovering something else. I can hear it again. The soft purr of the wolf.

I woke up on the morning I was meant to leave LA to go on this trip and still, with only hours before my flight, I hadn't packed my bag. Instead I sat silent before my bookshelf. It was so scarce of books, from so many moves, that on the bottom shelf sat my new meditation cushion and on the middle shelf I kept a simple altar with a little Quan Yin statue, the female Buddha. I usually sat before my bookshelf to meditate, but this time I sat on the cushion and looked to the middle shelf for my Italian great-grandfather's dictionary, sitting beside the goddess. He had bought it right before getting on a boat for Argentina, his new home, when he was young, for a better life. Some in my family say he was running away from the Masons whom he had joined. The dictionary still smelt like the inside of my grandfather's closet, his elegant wool jackets, a hint of cologne, and the chocolates that he hid in the drawer. I had never done this before, but I asked my bisnonno and his book if going to Italy was a good idea. I randomly flipped through it and the first word I read was "Transformazione," and then "Transizione."

This Saturday morning in my hotel room, I think of the ninety-two year-old Hungarian Jewish painter I used to work for in London when I first met Thomas. Her name was Suzanne and she painted up until her death at ninety-seven. Her depictions of London are colorful and vibrant. She was an apprentice of Oskar Kokoschka, the great Austrian painter, and was greatly influenced by him although her work was not as dark. Most of her paintings were intense but hopeful. My favorite of her works was a man, painted in blue, and we see only his back. He is moving against something; the strength in his movement is all I could see. She told me it was Jacob and the Angel. The painting is called "The Struggle for Identity." The Old Testament says that Jacob fought for a whole night with an angel. It was a long fight, but in the morning he prevailed. The angel gave him a new name. She had wanted to express how identity is a daily fight against all that the outside world tries to trap us into every day.

I get my running shoes on and head towards Ponte Vecchio. I pass by Pitti Palace and my favorite café where I used to go to do my work while Thomas was at his office when I was visiting in the summer. On the other side of the bridge I run past Uffizi Gallery where I will go tomorrow and then past all the touristy Florence sites until I reach the normal people streets and shops and cafés. The hills are not far. I imagine when the Renaissance buildings were being built, surprising the people from Florence, and also the time when they began to feel independent, at least the men.

Later that day near evening, right as I am about to go out, Thomas calls me on FaceTime, drunk in the streets of Krakow, asking how I am. He looks at me with love and I forget there is vodka here. I also forget he has met someone. We talk as if nothing has happened, but I do remember it all a minute later and I say I am off to dinner. As I leave the call, I wish I had asked him where that square was that we went to back in the summer, in the cool neighborhood with no tourists. It was lined with restaurants, a statue in the middle, full of locals and young people. I start to feel alone as I find nothing much on my street. I walk around to see what trattoria catches my eye and alas, I find myself in that exact square.

I ask a restaurant if they have a table.

"Per quanti?"

"Per una."

"Si!!! E si non l'habbiamo, la facciamo!" ("And if we don't have it we make it!")

Italy is friendly and lively and I have started to be hungry again. I sit at a table outside under the heater and two gorgeous young women sit at a table next to me. I start to wonder if I will run into his new girl. I tell myself I will see thousands of ragazze, and they will probably all be hot like young Claudia Cardinale, *so stop this right now.*

I cannot do much with my spaghetti pomodoro because I am only starting to eat again, but I have wine for the first time, since I also haven't drank for six weeks, as I had not wanted to get one bit sadder. I tell myself it is time to drink wine again. It actually makes me happier, and it makes me sleep all night.

Day 3 - Sunday

On Sunday morning I start with medieval paintings at the museum. Yes, I see how flat they are and how faces lack expression. Lots of Jesus. He was darker skinned back then.

146

Maybe that was more accurate. Moving on to the Renaissance. More Jesus. And a whole lot of Madonna e bambino, and everyone gets lighter and blonder. If I see another one I will scream about how dare these artists not tell us something else, and I will sound very ignorant. Also, artists had to eat and the church had the money. Maybe they hid the other stuff? I am dizzy with Madonna's, bambinos, Jesus and Apostles and before I scream I see a Madonna that looks different. Just incredibly beautiful. It's in the Botticelli section.

And that's where I see the painting *Primavera*. There is so much in it, and my audio guide tells me all about it: Venus is standing in the middle dressed in a beautiful robe, with a scarf on her head. Floating above her is the blinded cupid pointing an arrow. A monkey with a gun, kind of. Then Mercury on the far left, whom I see as a troublemaker because of astrologers warning you about Mercury retrograde and you losing objects and your shit. But he is just effortlessly pushing the clouds away with a sword so everyone can enjoy spring. Between him and Venus are three ladies dressed in white very gracefully dancing together, each representing an attribute I have not. One is Temperance and the others I cannot remember, but I didn't have either. On the other side of Venus is a woman who is touched by a blue-green frowning spirit coming out of the trees, floating. Is it a demon who is going to ruin Springtime? It turns out to just be a man, who by touching her, he makes plants grow out of her mouth and she turns into Spring herself.

Next to this is another painting, *Birth of Venus*, also by Botticelli. She is arising out of a seashell and her hair is coming out of the painting, full of light. I know just a few things about Venus. She is the goddess of love, beauty and abundance, sex workers, and sex. She is the goddess of many things.

I am about to leave as I have seen enough art for today when I feel myself suddenly guided back to her. I look into the eyes of the Venus of love and say to her in silence (wondering at what age I will start doing these things out loud), "Hi, Goddess Venus. Can I please ask for a favor? If it is not harmful to me or anyone, can you see if he can come back earlier? I don't know if I can still feel okay for four more days here waiting, as usual. I want all the waiting to end. Thank you."

Leaving the gallery, I stop at a painting that is hanging at a low level, close to the floor. It is a man lying on the ground bleeding, and a woman next to him holding a spear. The museum label explains that she is about to kill herself with it. Gregorio Pagani's *Pyramus and Thisbe*. Their story is the myth that Romeo and Juliet was based on. It looks more dramatic and visceral with a spear and blood than a little bottle of poison. The decision would have been a lot harder to make.

I leave the gallery, get changed, and take myself to a nice dinner on the other side of the Arno River, quite a walk away and also far from the touristy area, in a lovely and cozy restaurant I found online. There are white tablecloths and fairy lights on the ceiling.

"Havete tavola per una?," I ask.

They give me a table between the fireplace that has no fire and the bar. The waiter brings me a starter and a Prosecco "on the house" and, because I am "una," everyone comes to chat. The Brazilian waitress and I talk about leaving our countries, the changing environment of the economic crisis, as well as a desire for adventure. We share our stories and realize that both of us had an experience involving being robbed during a time in 2009 when the crisis in both our countries led to more street crime. Her story involved her father and two machine-guns, one to each side of his head. Mine involved a regular pistol to my throat and a kiss on the head by the robber.

"Where is your father now?" I ask and feel stupid as surely he is dead.

"He is in Rio."

Thank God.

"But I didn't want to live with that," she adds. "And he will never leave home. So that's how I ended up here all those years ago."

The owner comes to my table when he hears us talk. He is super friendly and eccentric, wearing many silver bracelets and rings on each finger, his longish silver hair elegantly combed back and a stature and elegant posture that would never go unperceived.

"¡Yo hablo Argentino!," he says in my own accent. He sits down and tells me how he went from Bolivia to the end

149

of Patagonia on a motorcycle and stayed in Argentina for too long because he did not want to leave.

"How did you manage the wind in Patagonia on a motorcycle?" I ask.

He looks for his phone and shows me a photo of a tree, its branches bent completely over to one side, like in a cartoon. "I often ended up on the opposite side of the road!"

I wonder how on earth does a tree do that? It must be extremely flexible. No other tree would grow in such a windy place.

After the starter, I cannot eat more than one big ravioli. My hunger is a work in progress. But I order lemon gelato and eat all of it. I am relieved I can live on this if all fails. Before I finish Thomas calls, saying he is on a train back from Poland. Thinking I was alone in Florence, it was not right that he was gone.

Grazie, Venus.

We make plans to meet the next day.

Facing the Streets of Firenze

Day 4 - Monday

Thomas finally shows up at lunchtime, after making me wait a few hours. He said he was nervous. I spend the morning in my hotel, after attempting a short run. I come back before I get anywhere because I don't want to be late. I had packed so quickly that I haven't brought more than a few changes of clothes. I wear my red V-neck sweater as it makes me look less tired. And more confident. He lets me know he has arrived and I open the big wooden hotel door downstairs and find him standing to the side of it, facing away from the hotel. I approach him. He gives me a strong hug and I turn around and start walking because I know how my emotions make him uncomfortable, especially if I cry. And I haven't been able to stop for a year.

We walk and start talking straight away, bursting with questions, apologies and forgiveness, or the illusion of it. We both want to be at peace. We cry often and stop to hug. As we walk the city I fear that we will bump into his new lover on every corner. That she will walk up beside us sitting against a window on the sidewalk. Maybe that is why he is taking my hand in the street and then releasing it.

"If you want to work on things, I will stay in Florence and not go back. I will move here," I say.

"Really?"

"Yes. I love you."

"What about your things?"

"I'll send for my things. Who cares about my things."

"What if you're not happy here? You'll blame me."

He tells me he is confused about his feelings towards me. He reminds me that he has just met someone. But in his face I also see love. Maybe it's my imagination, or some other kind of love he has for me now, which I really don't want to accept yet.

"You already told me you met someone. Stop saying that."

There is a pause.

"What, are you in love with her?"

"I don't know."

It didn't make sense. He told me that he just met her a few weeks ago. How could he be *in love* already? There was a lie here. Love at first sight is possible but I knew that breaking up with him on the phone back then was not crazy. And that even if I had come all the way here, he would not tell me the truth. I turn around to walk away towards my hotel, then stop after a few steps because during our last year living together I had started to walk away from him when I was hurt, sometimes to avoid exploding. I hadn't reacted explosively since I was twenty, when I could not control my emotions, until the last year of our relationship. I felt such impotence in many situations like when he came home drunk at 4 am after he said he would be home for dinner, and just laughed if I was upset. I had slapped his face then, and I surprised myself when I did. All those TV shows where the man does something outrageous and the woman slaps his face, then turns around and walks away. Do they ever show us that she feels any better? Countless scenes, comics. That was not the feeling I got. I do not want to react anymore, not even walking away. I stop and lean against the wall waiting for the physical sensation to pass, and he walks towards me.

"I just care for her. I think."

He takes me to lunch at that cool square, to a restaurant I liked so much during the summer. He says something and I hold his face with one hand. He has the most expressive face, which is a reason why I came. Five minutes later, he is holding my face across the table. We cannot eat. I have a huge plate of spaghetti in front of me and he has an almost full plate of ravioli. He asks what I am doing later. I say I have to leave to film an audition but can see him after that. He says he will film it with me as he always has done,

153

because my plan of piling up furniture and books together to lift the camera and FaceTiming my friend in LA to read with will be too difficult. He is right and also I don't want to be separated from him for one second.

We walk to my hotel. Coming in, the receptionist greets us with a grin. I feel like saying to him, "É solo un amico." He's just a friend. Which is what I am telling myself right now and it makes me dizzy. Two months ago Thomas was saying I was exactly what and whom he wanted, in a conversation in my LA kitchen, which never got to feel like our kitchen.

We go into my hotel room. I open the windows for light and I get my '80s top out of the closet to get changed for my scene, realizing I now should do this away from him in the bathroom, and that this was all a mistake.

I go through my clothes and ask him what he thinks of a dress I just bought while I take it out of the bag and put it into my suitcase. Why do I care about his opinion? I think of just saying that he should leave and I should FaceTime call my friend again, but then I will start crying, and I really don't want him to leave. I come out of the bathroom. He says I look nice and I roll my eyes without him seeing, because can this get any worse? He is relaxing, lying on my bed as if it is his. I want to lie there with him. I don't want to have sex. I just want us to hold each other through this thing we are going through. And the last thing I want to do right now is this audition.

He suddenly looks uncomfortable.

I say, "Are you sure you are okay with this? I don't know if I am. It feels really strange, doesn't it?"

"Come on, of course I am."

So we do the audition. He does a good job holding the camera with one hand and the paper to read lines with me with the other. I do my best but it's not good and it won't be because I am not there.

"Ok, I think that will do," I say. I go straight to the bathroom to get changed.

When I come back, he is looking in the mirror and asks what I think of his haircut. I wonder if he ever has looked past his reflection, inside his big eyes. Does he know what really is in there at all?

We both take a sweet from the reception desk and go through the glass door. He drops his sweet on the floor as he is unwrapping it, sulks, and goes back to the reception desk. I look at his sweet on the floor and back at him as he is picking a new one from the bowl. I pick it up, thinking of where I am can dispose of it, and put it in my pocket for now.

We go for ice cream and sit to eat it on some steps by the sidewalk when he says he doesn't like living in Florence because it is hard to make friends with people from the north of Italy. As well, it's difficult not speaking the language. Later we are having a cocktail in a restaurant downtown, one we have been to before a few times. I have a Milano Mule with vodka, ginger beer, and grapefruit juice, something I had never heard of outside of Italy. We are talking about our last year long-distance when he says, "It's over," out of the blue. It sounds forced and so unfamiliar, even if it has been over already.

"I understand. It's really over. Now please let's go." I get up and put on my coat.

"I am still not sure if I want to move to LA," he says.

"But it's over... So you won't."

"I am confused, I just don't want you to wait for me. And yes, I have met someone."

"You have said that already. Many times."

I want to walk by myself but he insists on walking back with me because it is late. I want to look for some takeaway food. I start feeling a sort of relief as we have reached an agreement, and I am hungry. He suggests we go to the little restaurant where they make gnocchi, my favorite food that is not easy to find in Florence. I cannot say no because even if I am fed up of all this, my heart still wants to attach itself to him. So we sit down. I order a giant gnocchi pomodoro plate and I eat the whole thing. We talk without tension for the first time. Without drama. About other things, eating and drinking wine until they close the restaurant. He leaves me at my hotel and we hug. When he turns to walk away I see he is crying. I start to feel it is really over. I needed to come here and feel it.

The Golden Moon
Day 5 - Tuesday

The following day I book a flight back to LA via two days with my friends in Barcelona, for the next morning. Then I go to see Venus to say thank you. This is probably some Catholic habit I have inherited from my abuela. I cannot not go. So I brave the tourists on the way there, imagining Florence with no people. I get very irritated trying to find the exit of the Uffizi after thanking the goddess, and I go straight to my favorite café, for more food.

He calls to see if I want to go for dinner with him.

Dear God, will this ever end? I thought we had said goodbye the night before. I had cried about it already. I tell him I am not sure because I love him and it would be hard to see him again.

My friends advise me not to go, one almost screaming at me on the phone, saying I should not be his doormat.

My friend is now actually calling me a doormat. She repeats again and again that he now has sex with another woman. "*Another woman*, get it?"

Obviously, but I decide I am going. I am feeling good that day, or maybe it is just the relief of that tension, all the questions and expectation gone.

We go to the first restaurant we went to in the summer. We meet and it feels like one of our first dates before any of this happened. We are attracted to each other. We laugh. We talk. We don't talk. He looks at me and I see more love in him now than I remember and I think maybe this is an encapsulated version so that I keep the good part. The waiter teases us. He steals a lot of my pasta and I remember what I don't like about him.

He says, "You know what I loved? Our..." and he cannot go on and breathes and looks away.

I breathe with him and say nothing and he changes the subject. He looks down and then at me and I see struggle in his eyes. The struggle he is going through inside. Or maybe his guilt. I say let's leave and he orders dessert.

He says he is going on a work trip the next morning, to the coast. I realize I am definitely still in love with him but that is okay and that will go away one day, and if it doesn't, love is infinite and I can love more people at the same time. I say I am jealous of his trip and he says I can come with him. But I remember I was not going to get on the roller coaster anymore and this is not a very clear invitation. It does not feel good. I remind him that my flight back, which he said I

158

should get, was now booked for tomorrow. He says nothing else, just looks down.

We end up staying until the restaurant closes again. We stay beyond closing, talking to the waiters and drinking amaro with them. They think we are a couple falling in love. We walk out and he suggests we go to the bridge near us one last time, to look at Ponte Vecchio. And there it is, lit under the full moon that faces us. Only six months earlier on this same spot he had asked me if I would like to have a Highland wedding. Now we sit in silence. I know I truly love him and he loves me, but I am done waiting. I have to learn to give up and no longer fight for it. I have to stop running from myself.

It becomes very warm and I open up my jacket as I sit on the bridge. Next to me, the Highland man so used to the cold has zipped his jacket up to his nose, literally. I almost laugh, and then also almost cry. He stares ahead, still the torment in his eyes. We are both staring at the full moon. It looks golden and Ponte Vecchio is golden beneath.

I have been stuck in a version of myself that is not real. I have to grow into myself, to see and accept my real self again. I have silenced the wolf in me but I can hear her calling. She is catching up to me, and in this moment I can release this self I have been trying to be and release him, into the water underneath us and transcend the past so I can fully become me.

The Italian Taxi Driver
Day 6 - Wednesday

I check out of my hotel in Via Romana. I have quite a few hours to wait until my flight to Barcelona. I go out and walk all the way to the arts center where I would have studied something like film or dance had I come to live in Florence, if I had chosen that other life. I want to see the place in case I want to come at another time. But mainly I want to see what I chose not to do. The life I will not live. I walk up to the opposite side of town, up a hill with bendy roads where little cars dodge me as I lean flat against a wall, thinking there must have been another way up for pedestrians but it is too late now.

I finally arrive at the beautiful villa. Again it looks like something out of a film. I am just hearing lots of loud and excited young voices in English that don't go with the light on the yellow building or the garden in the rolling Tuscan hills.

They don't let me in. I try asking the guy in the little cabin at the entrance that doesn't go with the building either, to please just let me have a look. It is all I need. "Per favoreeee."

Niente.

I go around the villa like a ghost trying to spy into the path I didn't take, now sweating under my black faux fur coat in the winter sun, until I find the proper entrance. I cannot go in without a student card here either. They tell me I should have called first. The man in this other cabin tells me how I can take a bus back, but I walk downhill, leaning against other walls, and finally through the city again. The city feels better.

At the hotel I get a change of clothes from my little suitcase, wash my face and armpits in the big bathroom near reception, and get dressed. I am late coming down to my taxi because I forgot my suitcase upstairs and have to go up again. When I reach the street, the driver is looking for me.

"Ciao! Scusa!"

"I was looking for you," he says in a strong accent, telling me off.

He is also on his phone, so barely looks at me while he takes my suitcase off my hands and puts it in the trunk of the car as if he was going to miss the flight himself. He is cute. Younger than me and surely thinks he is even more handsome than he is, I assume by his mood and arrogance. There is quite a bit of gel in his hair, but he is definitely hot. I realize I haven't looked at any men while I have been here. I forgot all about Italian men, too busy looking out for some ghost Italian ragazza whom I decided had taken my lover. I have forgotten about men in general. He starts the car, goes too fast while on his phone with his friend, and we almost crash. He lets go of his headphones, telling his friend that he has to go.

"Scusa. Drivers are crazy!" he says. "Did you see that?!"

"Va bene, non ti preoccupare."

"Ahhh! Ma tu parli italiano!"

"Si, un poco."

I tell him that I have forgotten a lot. His name is Maurizio. He asks why I came here and I try to tell him in my best Italian exactly why I did. Because I'll never see him again and I don't care what he thinks and I want to practice Italian for at least ten minutes. I think he understands what I am saying. He is friendlier than his original frown showed. Then he tells me about old Florentine winters, when people used to ski on Piazza Michelangelo, as we pass by. When he used to play in the snow. There used to be proper snow every winter. Now it is just cold without much fun. Global warming, he says in English. He asks me about Los Angeles.

When we get to the airport he ignores a call and asks me if I have time for a coffee. I have an hour. He takes my bag and leads me to his friend's café on the ground floor, facing the entrance. They have known each other since they were kids. His friend talks to me the entire time we are drinking our espressos, he does not leave us alone. The taxi driver is nervous; he is hesitant and so am I. He tells his friend we have to go and takes my bag as he leads me to security, and we wait at some seats until he gets in line with me.

"We should have left my friend's café earlier," he says.

I agree.

He gets closer to me and I wonder if he will just kiss me like only Italian men would do as soon as they meet you in the middle of the day. He is nervous again, stutters a bit. I hug him goodbye. We agree that I will practice my Italian with him on the phone and he will practice English with me, as he needs it for work. As soon as I cross security he texts me saying I should stay a few more days with him. He knows my flight out of Barcelona is a few days away, and he is still at the airport.

But I really don't know the taxi driver, and I am in a bit of a fragile state.

When I land in Barcelona that evening, Maurizio has sent me a photo. I realize that now I probably will be dating—I haven't in five years—and I am not sure I will ever be ready for it. I also wonder what he has sent me a photo of. I open it when I get to my friends' home. It is the sunset from a bridge. "Il tramonto," it says. The sunset. I have never heard that word.

Day 7 - Thursday

In the morning I walk to Barcelona's Miró museum. I am again going up a hill. I need to walk, to breathe, and to see art. It is as if going into someone else's dream world and out of mine is the only thing that will soothe me for a few minutes.

163

I look at Miró until I am tired. I sit in front of the yellow, asking it to cheer me up. There are lines, blue, stars, birds. If only there was this and not more to be connected to. For a moment, everything else falls away and I am in the universe of the painting. Nothing feels as good again. Not the view of the city from the terrace. Not the walk down, until while I am walking with no direction I come across the boardwalk by the sea. It is somehow very familiar. I see these steps down from a shopping mall onto the strip by the ocean. The image comes back. I once sat on those steps, probably at 4 am, out of that club inside the mall in the late 1990s. The big stairs are in front of me, to go in. I never thought of going back to this place. A sculpture has been built in the sea and extends out above the water. I don't remember it being there. I see the bench we all sat at more than twenty years ago with the first friends I made backpacking in Barcelona, when the building was brand new. I don't think I ever came here in the daytime. This club was where I saw the Polish girl dance like nobody was looking. I have now danced like her, fallen, got up, and danced again a million times. This is the first city I visited by myself as a backpacker where I didn't know anyone. Just me and my backpack and my book of hostels, and my fever from the nerves and excitement of an adventure alone, for the first time.

This time I have different luggage and a different uncertainty, but still the same curiosity with life.

Where am I going now? I have no idea. But will I go on my flight towards Los Angeles where I have made a new home.

It was the stories from my youth that made me stay where I was and forget myself. The same stories that repeated around me so long ago, and the voices in my head from the women in my family. They sound different now. And just as when I was seven and I prayed for the wolf who visited me to appear again, I knew it had the answers. I used to be afraid of the wolf, of her sure voice when she showed up facing the open door she would soon leave through. Now I recognize it, as strong as it used to be.

The Rising

Fooled

I arrive back in Los Angeles as skinny as when I left. My shoulders are sharp beneath my shirt. I go straight to a birthday party with circles under my eyes. Only upbeat music plays in my headphones on the way there and back.

I have a few commercial castings to go to on the following days, and I fight to show up. I put on the make-up, slip the heels into my bag, wear the clothes from my acting wardrobe for the characters I am asked to play again and again: School-run mum; smart-casual woman; office worker; ethnic mum (whatever that means to the people in the industry). I learn the lines and try to follow directions while I wish my real life to disappear. Every part of me is exhausted and it seems as if my body is shedding what I have tried to hold on to.

Being back in LA for a few months, once my real life has disappeared now under the first mandatory quarantine of 2020, I find it harder to escape any feelings that come up. Each wave is very clear as it arrives and as it leaves. It is good and it is bad.

I know I carry my mother's guilt. It is the guilt of women in general. We have been trained to please others and every time we refuse to do so, for many of us, something in the back of our brain still says, "Oh really? How dare you."

The guilt of deciding to go to Los Angeles for myself. I didn't want to have it but I watched myself feel this guilt and the one piled up in my DNA, built into a tower of shame.

My neighbor asks me to come and sit by our building's pool for a drink and cigarette. I bring the cigarettes as I have now started to smoke again. She brings the wine and cups that bear the logo of her fiftieth birthday party. She proceeds to tell me she has just ended an affair with a married man she loved. She then jumps into the pool with her clothes on, all romantic and spontaneous.

"Maybe they had an amazing connection," she says when I tell her that Thomas had met another woman before we broke up.

I think of her drowning, disappearing in the water, but more than that I want to sink deep into the water myself, deeper than the pool floor, and not come out.

I am forty years old and I live alone, in a studio apartment. If I was twenty-something and someone told me this would be my home life at forty, I would have told them to shut up. At least there would be one bedroom and a dog and I would go down the stairs to walk it in London or Paris. That is what I used to dream in my twenties. At forty I would be loving my house full of sunshine and probably a man I shared it with. I was never one hundred percent sure about having children; sometimes they were part of the picture. But I find myself at my table in the dining area adjoining the kitchen, from which I cannot but see half of my first decent bed.

Which I am really proud of, by the way.

I love my rented home. It is full of light, has wooden floors, and is a happy place to enter. It is quick to clean. I can pack up easily or just give it all away fast. This place is both half full and half empty. There is room to breathe and to walk freely. Room to still decide what to do with the space. I love the half empty part. It gives me freedom. The empty kind, maybe, but I really don't like clutter. There is still an echo. There are a few beautiful plants that I water once a week. I often bring home flowers. My bookcase is more than half empty and I will give away all the books when/if I leave the country again, except the ones that were gifts I didn't lose, like Joan Didion's *Slouching Towards Bethlehem*. A book of stories a Dominican writer sent me that I read for a podcast I was making. A collection of poems by female Beat Generation writers, and a book by my friend's father, about his mother who was also my friend.

The bathroom is my favorite room. It is pink in a 1930s style and the bathtub is so big I have to try not to slide and sink my head when I sit back. Judy Garland and Ava Gardner used to live two floors above. I didn't know this until the day I moved in.

I also have the vanity area with a mirror, as they did. The lights on it flicker sometimes. It is spooky and magical and tragic and glamorous in a simple way. On my first night I had a dream in which Mae West, whom I had just heard used to own the building, appeared on the ceiling above my bed, her giant face taking it all up in black and white, coming out of the ceiling as if from a screen and descending onto me. I love that I live in her building. That I look at myself in the same mirror that another actor has in the past, sharing their dream.

I have too many closets with not many clothes. I would leave tomorrow if you told me of a good place to go. Not just because right now I have become a little tragic like those actors in the 1930s really were or because Hollywood is dead, which I don't really mind. This place was always meant to be temporary. Now my contract is just up, and it would be the time I was going to move into a bigger place. A house. But not alone. The house I used to dream of. With light, a tree at the front, and flowers. But when it turned out to be just for me, as did all these closets, I didn't really want it. I have now remembered that I like changing scenes, and a house seems like an anchor, not roots anymore.

I turned my ex's closet into a recording studio even before we broke up, as if I knew he would not arrive and I had to do something about it. He replaced me around the same time. I got a pretty rug for the floor and isolation foam to transform the space. Now it just feels like a coffin inside.

Some days I want to be a nomad again, put everything in a car and live on the road. Maybe the reason I want this is to run from, or towards, me. Because I have kind of left the building of myself. Other days I am here, meeting my forgotten parts again. It's all floating.

Now I am being reminded of what I still want and who I really am as just me. Apart from wanting to move places because travel seems to be my karma, I have always longed for this life I would have if I was not a performer. I would live in the countryside. On a mountain. In a forest. At the beach. Of course that scene would also change. It is the life I have not yet lived. I could live out of the city. I don't know if it's a whim or a strong instinctual calling, a chance I have been waiting for without accepting.

Wild Animal Migration

I was looking at a very large piece of art in the Biennale in Kerala, India. It stretched from wall to wall. The setting was a forest filled with lots of trees and crows, painted in black and brown on a lighter background. An old man stood at the forefront, looking out at me. The crows were either flying or perched on a tree, many looking at a point in the painting's center. The gallery guide approached me to see if I wanted any information about it. He was a young man who studied film in Kochi and was working at the Biennale.

He explained that when a crow dies, groups of them gather around and stay near the scene. They look after the family of the deceased. Unlike humans, they stay long after the death to give support. I had only seen crows in London, sometimes in Battersea Park near my home, or by the Tower of London. They reminded me of ghosts and decapitation. We associate crows to things they have nothing to do with, because they are scavengers, don't chirp and are black like the supposed unlucky cat. Crows have been seen bending pieces of metal to make hooks, something not even apes do. Some migrate. Others don't. They are unpredictable.

Kerala was full of them. They would hang out at the beach, by the jungle, alone or in small groups. The day after I saw this painting, I found out I could finally move to Los Angeles. My visa had been approved after five years of trying.

Two months later, about two days after landing in Los Angeles, I had no energy to start a new life. How could I have been so mistaken? I had no interest in living for at least six months without my partner either. He would transfer later on, but nothing was certain in his world. I cried, got the flu, cried more. The lady from whom I was renting a room, Ángela, got me ramen, cold-pressed juice, and turmeric honey. She told me not to take any medicine. I took her advice. She is from Santiago, Chile. If you cross the Andes in a straight line from my hometown, you arrive at hers. She is a mother who now lives alone in her big home.

At the same time, a butterfly migration of Painted Ladies from Mexico was passing through Los Angeles on their way to Oregon, Washington, and even Alaska. They flew in groups of many, played around the garden, going fast and low around the streets, sometimes crashing against car windows. I could identify with the last part.

In the morning I was called outside by Ángela. Groups of crows were flying over the trees, mixing with enormous amounts of butterflies passing through, circling the garden.

"Did a crow die?" I asked.

She had no idea and was a bit weary of them. It was like a Hitchcock vs Disney situation. "Maybe there is a dead deer," she said. "But then they would gather to eat it." Her garden was on top of a hill full of trees.

The crows were loud. Those butterflies migrating, so pretty, so many. I thought of the percentage of them that would make it to where they were going. When one died crashing against something, the others carried on as if nothing had happened.

More than a year after my arrival in Los Angeles in 2020, I find myself sitting down to research the fauna that live in the Mayan Riviera jungle. I usually study the wild animals of wherever I am about to travel so I know what to do if I encounter them. So that I am not afraid, and because I always hope to find one.

When I went to India I learnt that some people who work in the jungle wear masks on the back of their heads. You must always face a tiger and never run or you will activate their chasing instinct and become prey. Unless the tiger is old and that instinct is off and you could be prey anyway.

Right now all I want is to be in a jungle by the sea. I am not going to think of why this is. When I feel something this strongly, I don't question it. I find out later. Maybe it's just a whim and I make up the rest. Either way, people do all kinds of things for all kinds of silly reasons. So what is taking off and going where you want? I'm from the opposite landscape of a jungle by the sea. I'm from a desert with altitude. And I have sat with myself too long.

I sell my first piece of furniture. The other chair. I keep one for now. I weep at night, and all morning. I wonder if I should ask for medication if I feel so sad for such a plain, almost new chair. I would if I had a nine-to-five job or a child. But I have no one to face. I am not grateful that "at least" I don't have children, as some say to me now. That at least I don't have to process a divorce. I am supposed to turn the page and go swiping. I'm going swimming.

I fall asleep thinking of clothes to give away and I wake up looking at the gold-framed mirrors from Morocco above my big plant. I think, I will take them down later. How could I forget? The bottom one is hung for my height, so I can look into it.

The old dreams must go and all the pretty objects I have been sitting amongst, which are connected to them. I sell the crystal coffee table, my favorite piece of furniture. I found it downstairs in my building with a note that said, "Free." I will get the same one next time if I can. I don't cry, but it is not easy. I have moved homes many times and this is the first time I love my furniture. I have never cared before. Not for one second. It still is the most ridiculous idea to me, but it is happening. I watch myself as I kiss my table good-bye. I am going insane and nobody's looking.

Now I understand how my ex felt when we left the Madrid apartment and he asked me to keep it one more month, refusing to sell the sofa yet, even if we were not living there anymore. That was where his heart broke, and I didn't see it.

My friend Chloe comes to visit. She wants my big plant if I am going to give it away. She has the same one and wants a companion for it. So my plant goes with her into a family home. Even though I give it an embarrassing hug, I am glad we are all moving. The crying has stopped like the end of a tango. I am scared it will start again but we are so bored of each other, I doubt it.

Now that almost all the things are gone I am in that familiar place of a backpack and two suitcases. I feel more myself. It is a relief. The emptier it gets, the better I feel. It cures me. How can it be? I used to think I was like a Greek soul that did something very bad because I am always roaming. But those souls are supposed to be permanently suffering. I suffer when I stay too long in one place.

I thought turning forty would change me into someone else. I see it has not yet. Maybe I will never grow up. Maybe maturing is to think even less and follow myself even more. My empty place is my space between chapters, and I like open space.

Back to the Jungle

I sit on my balcony looking at the jungle in my new neighborhood, back in Latin America. As soon as I arrived I felt relieved and safe, even though everyone tells me to be careful because I am a woman on my own. Just listening to Spanish and the Mexican accent is soothing, the Caribbean Sea nearby, the humid heat. The birds are loud and many, celebrating the morning with all their different sounds blending in. Then the men at the construction site near me arrive, start hammering, and the birds wind down. It is the turn of the builders now that the sun is fully up. I curse them for a moment as I grab my tea to go inside. Then I remember that I myself am under demolition and construction, so who am I to complain?

I am in Tulum, a town by a jungle and, unless I go much deeper in and live even more isolated, this is what there is. So I begin to get up earlier, to be on the balcony at sunset, to hear the birds and let their song go through me like a sound bath. I have only a few neighbors because of the pandemic, but the locals love to put on their music and have parties, and soon I see that quite a few musicians live here. I decide to enjoy the neighbor with the electric guitar, and the reggaetón from the other neighbor. I rest. I sleep. I am still not back into cooking, but I rediscover Mexican food and it is still my favorite in the world. Real tortillas made by hand, chilaquiles, real cacao, which smells like greens. I have an all right kitchen, just in case.

The trucks pass by with their megaphones advertising water, gas, all kinds of services with songs. My favorite is the bread man, el panadero. And my favorite panecito is the one made with sweet potato. I run outside or chase him down on my bicycle if I am in the street. These are about the only people I speak to as there is still nothing much open.

When I step onto the beach I have arrived in paradise. I am in another dimension. The white sand, the jungle behind it, and the crystal clear water. I go deep in and swim and float and it is like being in a Van Gogh painting. The water moves and the sky is reflected on it. I never took the time for this and I know I am lucky to have this time. I feel happy and fragile at the same time. Will I ever emerge from the water like a goddess.

I make an altar on my wooden desk in my room with

the balcony. This is the first thing that makes any place my home. I put on it a few rocks and crystals, my little Quan Yin statue made of Tiger Eye crystal that a friend gifted me. I add a big candle because the light goes out here all the time. A Virgin Mary stamp another friend gave me years ago that will not last on this desk long but I am drawn to all these female archetypes lately so I let them exist there. My altar keeps changing. I ride my bicycle to the beach and around town. I am happy on a bicycle. It connects me to childhood fun.

At home I cry. I feel relief. I rest. I torment myself, I find peace. All the ups and downs of mourning. I wonder why I ended up here. If I could have done things differently. Maybe if I had not been so stubborn and had just gotten married. If I had never gone to LA. What would the eleven-year-old girl who caught the bouquet think of me now? Am I leaving her alone or am I taking her hand? But mainly I am safe with myself, by myself. I begin to be at peace more and more often.

I can live in and enjoy solitude. It is my comfort zone. But I begin to feel a loneliness that tells me I have been secluded long enough now. I have felt it before. I recognize it.

A hurricane is approaching and I am excited because I have never been in one, and although we are told that we will be fine, it turns out to be rougher than anyone expected. The wind gets loud, its whistling insistent, and as I watch the flexible and unruly jungle trees protect the place I live in, brushing the balcony and windows, I watch a few fall, or be cut in half. My balcony is full of branches and water hits the windows. At one point I close all the curtains and put chairs against the long windows as if that could do anything. I have prepared with a bit of food and maybe too many sweets as I got excited in the market queue watching other people buy things. I got two extra candles. This night that I am inside I realize that I have not laughed in a month. This is why I am sad. I need to go outside and meet other people. It is time for me to come out of my cave.

A few weeks later I have a message on my phone from a friend of a friend from Argentina. He is a musician coming to Tulum hoping to find work as the town begins to open, before the rest of the world does. He says he doesn't know anyone here. We agree to meet even though it is raining. He arrives with a plastic poncho, carrying another one for me, but I am now so used to the rain that I don't bother to put it on. We have a beer at this place on my street where I have been wanting to go with company.

In the following weeks something happens in me that I was not expecting. I begin to see theatre happen wherever I go, in my mind. Is this because I am beginning to choose to be around people again? I have been happy to leave that part of myself, who I was as an actress. I want to forget her. Maybe I am not an actress anymore. I want to be nothing in particular. Start at zero. Be myself without any labels attached. But as I sit at a hotel restaurant looking out to sea with a pool between us, I cannot but imagine a family around this pool and an uncomfortable silence in a dramatic scene, actors in and out of the water. Maybe it is a musical, actually. And it is not a family. I tell myself to stop, to forget it. It must be my wired brain telling me I should start working again. Then I am at the beach alone and I begin to see another scene in my mind. A site-specific show at sunset, in and out of the jungle. The audience is led inside and can move around while the actors are living the scene, moving between vegetation and sand and maybe even the water. Why is my brain doing this? Why can I not just stop? The images appear in my mind, compelling. They do not leave me alone. Is this what being an artist is? Are our brains wired to make something poetic happen, or am I picking up on something in the air. Being here in nature and on my own road, am I opening to some playful spirits?

In a few days my longing to put on a show near the water is so loud it does not let my mind rest. Like an aching. I tell my friend that I need to find performers. I have accepted it. A few days later, a couple I have just met tell me that they have seen a theatre performance recently, which took place at the new co-working space in the evening. They loved it. I ask them to please send me the details. Before they do, the next morning I go to a local book-filled café, the sort of town library. I sit with my diary but cannot write. I am restless. Two people sit in front of me, chatting in Spanish. She is Argentinian and he is Mexican. She is lively and has a young but sure voice. He is calm and speaks slower, engaged in their conversation. They begin to talk about a venue and how the place took most of the money, so it is best if they try somewhere else. She says they need to keep up the training. Then an Uruguayan guy sits next to them and says he is soon going back into the jungle for a while, so they should get together and figure out when rehearsals will be. This must be them, the actors. I want to hear more about the jungle. Where is he going back to? I wonder if he has seen a jaguar there. Another one arrives, a Mexican girl who sits right next to me and soon a very quiet man from the US sits on the floor on my other side. I realize I am sitting in a circle with the local theatre company. I offer the man on the floor my seat as I am in their meeting. I will go to the next room.

"No, please, he likes the floor," says the Mexican guy.

"Stay with us, really," says the girl next to me and I immediately wish she was my friend. I ask if they are the theatre company I have just heard about and wanted to meet since last night.

"You manifested us," says the Uruguayan. We laugh. They are planning a new show. The theme will be water. I hear myself say I am an actress without a single doubt. They say they need one, and that I am already with them, since I am attending the first meeting about the new show.

The Argentinian girl says, "When can you start?"

"Wait, what if she doesn't like what we do," says the Mexican guy and they invite me to see their show the next week.

I walk into a dome-shaped building with big 1960s futuristic windows looking at the jungle, part of a fancy Tulum hotel at the edge of the pueblo. The low cushioned seats for the audience, which are normally used for meditation, are placed in a circle inside. The first scene begins. The Mexican actor goes into the circle to do a monologue in Spanish. It is a comedy and it is brilliant.

The actors outside the circle provide sound effects. This time it is hens. The character is alone in a hut in the jungle going insane. The next scene is in English with him, the US guy, and Mexican girl. Then the Uruguayan and Argentinian girl tell a completely different story about a couple on holiday in the middle of a hurricane. The audience is a mix of tourists and Mexicans. I can tell some don't speak Spanish and some don't speak English, but it doesn't matter. The actors and the stories are good. I become slightly scared to join them. I stay and wait for the actors after the show ends.

"So, are you joining us?" asks the Mexican guy, who runs the company.

We all go into the pueblo for dinner and drinks and soon spread out into the streets. I join a part of them in a restaurant, and then another in a garden bar, until we hear from someone in a club that the civil guards are near. They are looking at people's passports, so we all go back to the street to tell the Uruguayan guy that he has to run because his visa has just expired. The guys in the company make sure he is gone by the time the police arrive in their big military van. By then we are all spread out again and it is late. I go to find my bicycle to get home, feeling a new sense of belonging in the town as I ride back in the dark.

The Square

The big square is empty again as I find it on my way home. It is almost midnight and this seems to be a new routine. I have been walking alone at night, usually after meeting friends, because I enjoy it and other times because I don't want to be alone in my home just yet. Here loneliness has company, colors, warm air, and music everywhere. Here street dogs are everybody's company. Late at night the streets are quiet, as I am most of the time, and I enjoy the bad lighting as I walk. I go by the sushi place that is at the end of downtown, the "centro," before the streets become dirt in my neighborhood and my sandals and feet get dirtier. I take a cup of lemonade with ice for the long walk back. Sometimes I just go all the way to the centro and straight back home, stopping at the square. It opens like a big, inviting patio, with trees on its sides, now surrounded by the closed bicycle shops and the taco stands that are packing up except for the one that waits a little longer. I ask the guy in charge if he has a lighter, again. My other new but old habit I would like to kick. I look at the square with the church at the back, which you would never guess is a church. No cross or obvious symbols. It looks just like a house with its dirty pink and white paint and concrete benches extending from the walls. I sit there with my lemonade and my cigarette, enjoying the silence and the late hour in which nothing is supposed to happen. It is past midnight, and someone is sleeping on another bench near me. The mosquitoes don't bite me anymore. I am now part of the tropics. The starry sky can be seen, unlike the skies of all my insistent years in cities. Sometimes I miss them. I miss dressing elegantly. And if I was there now I would miss my uncombed hair of seven months and my clothes that float around my body because I cannot bear any other clothes.

Today I tried on my abuela Lolita's rock-crystal necklace. It was in the little box where I keep my valuables. She always wanted to come to Mexico and never did. Maybe she is with me now. I looked in the mirror. What elegance! Maybe I will wear it again one day here, or in a city, if the jungle ever spits me out. Which I doubt because we are very close now. I cannot imagine my life without her for more than a few days. She protects me like the mountains in a lighter way. On the outside she moves, feminine against the storm. Inside she holds secrets guarded by the jaguars and the serpents, the gods. They are the jungle, dying and flowering. Just like our parts that die and are born again.

Epilogue

My new musician friend invites me on a day trip into a jungle town, to visit a Mayan family for lunch. We arrive later than we planned, but when we enter the main hut the grandmother returns to her fire to make more tortillas for us. She uses yellow corn meal made by the women in the family. She invites me to try making a tortilla myself. I watch how she uses her hands and try to replicate her movements.

We eat. I even try the pork after being vegan for eight months. The men in the family kill the animal themselves and the women use every part, cooking with gratitude and with such enjoyment and this way I will eat animals.

After lunch everyone relaxes. We chat sitting inside the hut where we have eaten. Next to us is the little house they share, and outside facing the road is another area for cooking where more women are preparing a chicken for tonight. It is the festivities of La Virgen de Guadalupe. Also facing the road is the family's outdoor chapel that features colorful wooden benches and traditional decorations. I go outside to wave at cars with the children, who wait for candy to fly out of the car windows as the drivers and passengers pass by, only on this day. Each of the five children all go back inside with quite a few sweets. I stop to sit on the chapel benches next to my friend. It is quiet and warm. We stay there in silence looking at the Virgen for a while before going back into the shade of the hut.

The women bring out bags of vegetables to be cut for tonight's boiled chicken and tomorrow's cochinita pibil, a slow-cooked pork dish made in the "pib" oven outside under the ground, consisting of hot stones. The women sit on low stools in the hut, peeling and cutting the vegetables on a small, low table. I offer my help. My friend lays on a hammock in the middle while they give me the knife that is left, the ordinary one you use for cutting meat on your plate. I look at the size of the small pieces they cut so I will make the same. They laugh when I peel a potato with that knife and we all agree I will stick to cutting.

The youngest girl keeps being told that day by the guy who took us there, to go to the city to work and make money as she has a great personality and is very clever. But she says she is happy helping out her aunt who really needs her. They are all bilingual in Spanish and Mayan but say just a few Mayan words among themselves as we sit, commenting on the kids moving around, playing men killing men with chess pieces on the floor. Their smiles always wide and bright, always joking with each other. We fall into silence, working with the rhythm of a well-oiled machine. We cut the potatoes and carrots and throw them into the pan across the table from me, for hours. I have to stand and try to aim with my cupped hands. More veggies keep coming. Some women swap places around me. I look up occasionally and see a different face in front of me or by my side, and I keep going. The energy in our circle is so tranquil that I don't realize how much time has gone by.

When all the vegetables are cut I look up and see my friend is up from his siesta, not on the hammock anymore. He is holding a can of beer and I ask for a sip, the cold metal soothing my sore hand. I now want a cigarette. He goes outside to try to buy some, but one of the men hears him and gets him one. I come out of the hut and we are sharing a cigarette when we are called by the men who are sitting next to the pib ovens behind the hut, looking after the fire. They all sit in a circle. My friend sits and I stand right outside of it as this is the men's circle and I don't want to intrude. But a few seconds later someone calls my friend over from the other side of the patio and the men insist I sit in the empty chair. I try to get comfortable but also don't want to get too comfortable. I have been there a minute and am getting up when the older man gets up himself and offers me a new cigarette so I will smoke one more with them. We have a conversation. The energy is different than in the women's circle, but it is still light. I keep thinking I don't belong there but then I look at my legs. They are spread out and crossed at the ankles. I am lying back and relaxed among them, enjoying my cigarette. They keep telling me how much they enjoy when friends visit. One of them repeats to me that he wants to go into the city to work. He wants to learn English. He drops his cigarette when he says it and doesn't bother picking it up. He has had a few drinks, it seems. My friend comes to get me then as we were leaving. I stand up and say thank you. As I sit in the car I see the blister forming on the bottom of my index finger from the pressure of the knife, a tender red area around it. I have never had something like this happen from preparing food, though surely I have participated in big party cooking. I used to help my grandmother peel tomatoes for her sauce, but I was a child and I would get bored and find an excuse to leave too soon. There is something about cutting vegetables in squares, for me. Like when I make soup for myself or someone else. When you cook with love and dedication. There was a love to what the women were doing, a feeling of home and belonging, which they shared with their visitors. And I had put my love into the chore, hypnotized by the circle. I belonged for that time, as I have in many circles before since I was born. The circle of my family, of my school friends, of the travelers and artists with whom I have felt safe to be myself. The circles that have always appeared wherever I go. The ones I leave when I hear my calling. The ones I have insisted on when I was not living truthfully and the ones I am part of from wherever I am.

We are headed down on the road to the sea, stopping at the pueblo, my home for now. For now, I repeat to whoever asks me about my plans because as much as I feel it is my home, I don't have a plan. For now this place has welcomed me and I have belonged here. I am a nomad, and I also settle. I know I carry my home with me, but now I am listening to the moment. I feel movement in me, perhaps because I am in a town by the sea, with rain, and water underneath the stone ground.

For now I am grateful to be in Latin America where my blood has a root, and I felt its pull and I followed it as I will follow the current that goes through me. I trust it now, like the smallest wave can feel the force of the ocean arriving at the shore.

Most sincere thanks to Mick Thyer and his Writer's Workshop, to Kym Allen and Jana Krumholtz for leading me to write, and to Manuela Gomez Rhine, Julia Rufener and Alexa Ashley.

About the Author

Dolores Reynals was born in Mendoza, Argentina. She started out as a radio actress before moving to London to attain her BA (Hons) in Drama from the University of Surrey. Since then she has worked internationally and now lives between Europe and Mexico.

This book was set in Garamond Premiere Pro, a typeface designed by Robert Slimbach based on the designs of Claude Garamond from the 1500s. Helvetica Neue is the header font and was designed by Max Miedinger. The cover design is by Julia Rufener and the book design is by Alexa Ashley.

9 786072 953123